The New McGraw-Hill Exercise Book
to accompany

The New McGraw-Hill Handbook
and
A Writer's Resource

Prepared by

Santi Buscemi
Middlesex County College

Susan Popham
University of Memphis

With editorial consultant

Karen Wink
United States Coast Guard Academy

Boston   Burr Ridge, IL   Dubuque, IA   Madison, WI   New York   San Francisco   St. Louis
Bangkok   Bogotá   Caracas   Kuala Lumpur   Lisbon   London   Madrid   Mexico City
Milan   Montreal   New Delhi   Santiago   Seoul   Singapore   Sydney   Taipei   Toronto

The McGraw·Hill Companies

The New McGraw-Hill Exercise Book
Buscemi and Popham

Published by McGraw-Hill, an imprint of The McGraw-Hill Companies, Inc., 1221 Avenue of the Americas,
New York, NY 10020. Copyright © 2007, by The McGraw-Hill Companies, Inc. All rights reserved.

1 2 3 4 5 6 7 8 9 0 QPD/QPD 0 9 8 7 6

ISBN-13: 978-0-07-326032-7
ISBN-10:   0-07-326032-0

www.mhhe.com

The New McGraw-Hill Exercise Book for use with *The New McGraw-Hill Handbook*, first edition, and *A Writer's Resource*, second edition

Table of Contents

EDITING FOR GRAMMAR CONVENTIONS

EDITING FOR CLARITY

EDITING FOR CORRECTNESS: PUNCTUATION, MECHANICS, AND SPELLING

To the Student

This book has been organized for use with the first edition of *The New McGraw-Hill Handbook* and the second edition of *A Writer's Resource* by Elaine P. Maimon, Janice H. Peritz, and Kathleen Blake Yancey. Each exercise begins with a reference to the section(s) of the handbooks to which the exercise corresponds. You can refer to these sections to find more information and suggestions for dealing with the sentence problems covered in each exercise. In addition, the "Using Catalyst" box at the beginning of each exercise refers you to your handbook's Web site for additional resources.

As you complete these exercises, you can check your work by referring to the Answer Key at the back of the book. Possible answers to the editing exercises and answers to the pretest and posttest are available to instructors at **www.mhhe.com/nmhh** or **www.mhhe.com/awr**. You should also see if you can apply the rules you have practiced here to your own writing.

PRETEST

Items 1–5: Sentence Parts

Instructions: The following items ask you to identify various parts of a sentence. Write your answers in the spaces provided.

EXAMPLE

Find a conjunction:

The soldiers had marched all night, and they were tired.

and

---

1. **Find the sentence's subject and verb:**

   The book contained controversial materials.

   _____   _____
   sub   verb

2. **Find a pronoun and an adverb:**

   Venice, which is on the Adriatic, was once mistress of the seas.

   _____   _____
   pron   adv

3. **Find an adjective and a preposition:**

   Shouting to the audience, he made a grandiose gesture, which proved his arrogance.

   _____   _____
   adj   prep

4. **Find a subordinate clause:**

   I get a terrible rash whenever I eat chocolate.

   _____

5. **Find a main clause:**

   After going deaf, Beethoven continued to write music that the world still loves.

   _____

Items 6–20: Sentence Structure and Logic

Instructions: The following items contain three versions of the same sentence or sentences. Write the letter of the best version on the line to the right

---

EXAMPLE

a. A bear ate our food while we camped in the woods.
b. While camping in the woods, our food was eaten by a bear.
c. Our food was eaten by a bear while camping in the woods.

_____*a*_____

6.　　a. For me, learning math is difficult therefore, I devote more time to it than to other subjects.
　　　b. For me, learning math is difficult, therefore, I devote more time to it than to other subjects.
　　　c. For me, learning math is difficult; therefore, I devote more time to it than to other subjects.

_____

7.　　a. It was cold and windy outside the house was warm and tight.
　　　b. It was cold and windy outside, but the house was warm and tight.
　　　c. It was cold and windy outside, the house was warm and tight.

_____

8.　　a. We sat behind Jim Maria sat in front.
　　　b. We sat behind Jim and Maria sat in front.
　　　c. We sat behind Jim, and Maria sat in front.

_____

9.　　a. Soccer is a popular sport in many countries one can find fans who are devoted to it.
　　　b. Soccer is a popular sport, in many countries one can find fans who are devoted to it.
　　　c. Soccer is a popular sport; in many countries one can find fans who are devoted to it.

_____

10.　　a. While waiting to be called on, my foot fell asleep.
　　　b. My foot fell asleep while waiting to be called on.
　　　c. My foot fell asleep while I waited to be called on.

_____

11.　　a. Shocked by the startling news, everyone in the house became quiet.
　　　b. Everyone in the house shocked by the startling news became quiet.

2

c. Shocked by the startling news, the house became quiet.

_____

12. a. Basque is spoken in an area of Spain, but it is unrelated to Spanish.
    b. Basque is spoken in an area of Spain it is unrelated to Spanish.
    c. Basque is spoken in an area of Spain, it is unrelated to Spanish.

_____

13. a. China has the largest population. Followed by India.
    b. China has the largest population, followed by India.
    c. China has the largest population, it is followed by India.

_____

14. a. The wine spilled over the embroidered white tablecloth immediately turned red.
    b. The wine spilled over; the embroidered white tablecloth immediately turned red.
    c. The wine spilled over the embroidered white table cloth; immediately turned red.

_____

15. a. Mozart was a child prodigy however, he also died quite young.
    b. Mozart was a child prodigy; however, he also died quite young.
    c. Mozart was a child prodigy, however, he also died quite young.

_____

16. a. Our students have been tutored by Paula, Mike, and Matt for weeks.
    b. By Paula, Mike, and Matt, our students have been tutored for weeks.
    c. For weeks, our students by Paula, Mike, and Matt have been tutored.

_____

17. a. On the phone she apologized to her professor for her paper, which was smeared with ink and covered with coffee stains.
    b. She apologized to her professor for her paper on the phone, which was smeared with ink and covered with coffee stains.
    c. On the phone she apologized for her paper to her professor, which was smeared with ink and covered with coffee stains.

_____

18 a. Bob found two empty coolers walking across the parking lot into the stadium to watch the football game.
   b. To watch the football game, Bob found two empty coolers walking across the parking lot into the stadium.
   c. Walking across the parking lot into the stadium to watch the football game, Bob found two empty coolers.

_____

19. a. Natalie hates flying and avoids driving.
     b. Natalie hates to fly and avoids driving.
     c. Natalie hates flying and avoids to drive.

     _____

20. a. Solar heating for a large building is technically different from a single-family home.
     b. Solar heating for a large building is technically different from that for a single-family home.
     c. Solar heating for a large building is technically different from single-family homes.

     _____

Items 21–35: Correct Usage

Instructions: Correct any problem you find in the following sentences by rewriting the part of the sentence that is incorrect. Place your corrections in the spaces to the right. If the sentence is correct, write *C* in the space. <u>Note:</u> You may have to change or add words.

EXAMPLE

Save the planet; our children's future depend on it.

                                                   *depends*

---

21. The Soviet Union were a coalition of several Asian and European states by Moscow.

     _____

22. The computer and the fax machine has made our lives a lot easier.

     _____

23. Ari's friend and confidant are Melissa.

     _____

24. After laying down for only a few minutes, I heard the phone ring.

     _____

25. The Environmental Committee debate questions on water and air pollution.

     _____

26. Someone have written silly notes on the bus station wall.

     _____

27. Neither the Mendozas nor their son are here.

     _____

28.   Each of the people at the meeting have a child in this school.   _____

29.   Either Sam or Ted will lend us their car.   _____

30.   Everyone in this class wants his cake even after having eaten it.   _____

31.   By the time I got to the store, it was closed for hours.   _____

32.   Before she started law school, she wanted visiting Yellowstone National Park.   _____

33.   They claiming that I am lying is quite ironic.   _____

34.   Felicia and her went to school together.   _____

35.   She doesn't have a prejudice bone in her body.   _____

Items 36–45: Punctuation, Spelling, and Mechanics

Instructions: Correct the following sentences by adding or removing punctuation, correcting spelling, or making other changes. Rewrite each sentence correctly on the lines that follow it.

> **EXAMPLE**
>
> Mythology is one way a culture explanes its values.
>
> *Mythology is one way a culture explains its values.*

36.   The instructor asked us to read Poe's short story The Telltale Heart but I read Welty's A Worn Path instead.

_____

37.   Where have all the young men gone

_____

38.   She has to complete her term paper tonight so she can't go to the movies.

_____

39. Adriana is not my neice, she is my cousin.

_____

40. The headwaiter at the gluttonous gourmet restaurant said he could accomodate our ten person party.

_____

41. This weeks paycheck should be larger than usual.

_____

42. Theres only one thing I hate arrogance.

_____

43. 340 cavalrymen charged the cannons at full gallop.

_____

44. In her geography class, Phyllis learned that her dog belonged to a breed that took its name from Chihuahua Mexico.

_____

45. After eating the dog lay down in a corner of the living room and fell asleep.

_____

Items 46–47: Writing Essays

Instructions: Read each item carefully. Then choose the best response, and write its letter in the space to the right.

46. Which of the following would make the best thesis statement for an essay of between 500 and 750 words?

a. The causes of the American Civil War.
b. One cause of the American Civil War was the insistence of some Southern leaders that the states were sovereign entities.
c. Several factors, including the debate over slavery, the question of state's rights, the changes caused by a rapidly growing economy, all contributed to the outbreak of the American Civil War.

_____

47. Which sentence does not belong in the paragraph? Write its letter in the space provided.

(a) *Some international students at our college are having trouble adjusting to our culture.* (b) *Many of them find that the food in our cafeteria is not in keeping with the dietary laws they followed in their countries.* (c) *American students seem addicted to fast foods such as hamburgers, french fries, and pizza.* (d) *Some immigrants also have a hard time understanding our dating customs.* (e) *Still others find the cost of living here quite high.*

_____

Items 48–50: Writing Research Papers

Read the following entry from the *Reader's Guide to Periodical Literature,* and answer the questions that follow. Write the correct answers in the spaces provided.

> **BLACK HOLES (ASTRONOMY)**
>   Biggest black hole in the universe? J. Horgan. il. *Scientific American*
>   265:32 Jl '91

48. Who is the author of this article? _____

49. In what month and year was the article published? _____

50. In the spaces below, write an entry for this article as it would appear in a works-cited page, which uses the Modern Language Association (MLA) format.

_____

_____

End of Pretest

EXERCISE 1: WRITING PAPERS – THESIS DEVELOPMENT

CORRESPONDS TO SECTION 3B IN *THE NEW MCGRAW-HILL HANDBOOK* AND SECTION 5C IN *A WRITER'S RESOURCE*

USING CATALYST	www.mhhe.com/nmhh www.mhhe.com/awr
For help with developing a thesis, go to Writing > Paragraph/Essay Development > Thesis/Central Idea	

Instructions: Read each set of three statements below. Decide which item would make the best central idea (a thesis statement that is neither too broad nor too narrow) for an essay of between 500 and 750 words. Write its letter in the space to the right.

EXAMPLE

    a. Measures we can take to prevent the spread of AIDS.
    b. Defeating AIDS means prevention.
    c. Defeating AIDS through preventive measures.   *b*

---

1. a. Smoking cigars can be dangerous.
     b. The dangers of smoking cigars.
     c. Second-hand cigar smoke and second-hand cigarette smoke pose similar health hazards.

                                                             _____

2. a. Giovanni Lorenzo Bernini, a sculptor and architect, was popular with many prominent leaders of seventeenth-century Italy.
     b. Giovanni Lorenzo Bernini designed churches, chapels, and tombs for several popes.
     c. Giovanni Lorenzo Bernini invented an exciting type of sculpture that broke with the mannerist tradition popular during the early part of the seventeenth century.

                                                             _____

3. a. The cell is the basic unit of structure in biology.
     b. The basic structure of all living cells includes a membrane, cytoplasm, and a nucleus, each of which performs a different function.
     c. A protozoa is a single-celled organism.

                                                             _____

4. a. In *Anatomy of an Illness as Perceived by the Patient*, Norman Cousins argues that a patient must take some responsibility for his or her recovery from an illness.

b. *Anatomy of an Illness as Perceived by the Patient* is a well-known book by Norman Cousins, who was a controversial editor of the *Saturday Review* for more than thirty years.

c. Norman Cousins, who edited the *Saturday Review* for more than thirty years, wrote a book about how he overcame a serious illness contracted in 1964.

_____

5. a. Among the chief tenets of fascism is a belief in the racial superiority of one people over all others.

b. Nazism is a form of fascism.

c. The Nazis believed in and practiced anti-Semitism.

_____

6. a. Ivan IV ruled Russia in the sixteenth century.

b. The policies of Czar Ivan IV of Russia earned him the title "Ivan the Terrible," demonstrating that he was an unsuccessful and unpopular leader.

c. Ivan, who had been Grand Duke of Moscow, secretly arranged to have himself crowned czar in 1547.

_____

7. a. The Ivory Coast, located in western Africa, achieved independence from France in 1960.

b. Since independence in 1960, the Ivory Coast has experienced healthy economic growth chiefly because of its exports of coffee, cocoa, and timber.

c. Although many Europeans traveled to the Ivory Coast, the Portuguese began the horrific practices of trading in ivory and slaves.

_____

8. a. Many young people get their morality, not from their parents or their religion, but from the popular media.

b. Morality is defined as the concept of being right or wrong.

c. Few people ever try to assess, critique, or understand the moral code they follow.

_____

9. a. Hypertension, or high blood pressure, is known as "the silent killer" because few people recognize its symptoms.

b. The most effective treatment for hypertension includes following a low-sodium diet, taking medications such as beta blockers and diuretics, and using biofeedback.

c. Prolonged hypertension can lead to a number of serious medical consequences.

_____

10. a. Runes are characters used in early Germanic inscriptions.

b. Many scholars believe that runic characters, which first appeared around the third century BC, were derived by the Ostrogoths from alphabets used in Hellenic-Italic languages.

c. Runic inscriptions were still being made in Scandinavia during the Middle Ages, even though much of the rest of Europe no longer knew of their existence.

_____

EXERCISE 2: WRITING PAPERS – THESIS DEVELOPMENT

CORRESPONDS TO SECTION 3B IN *THE NEW MCGRAW-HILL HANDBOOK* AND SECTION 5C IN *A WRITER'S RESOURCE*

Instructions: Using the topics below, construct an effective thesis statement for each topic. Keep in mind that a thesis statement should be neither too broad nor too narrow, should name the topic of the paper, and should be arguable.

1. Requiring college students to purchase laptops in order to attend college

_____

_____

_____

2. Requiring young children to be vaccinated before entering public school

_____

_____

_____

3. Expensive licensing fees for owners of pit bulls

_____

_____

_____

4. The death penalty for juveniles who commit murder

_____

_____

_____

5. Prohibiting teenagers and children from using tanning beds

_____

_____

6. Limiting all publicly elected officials to a maximum of two terms in office

_____

_____

_____

7. Raising the cigarette tax

_____

_____

_____

8. Prohibiting the use of cell phones, handheld personal digital assistants, and laptops in college classrooms

_____

_____

_____

9. Metal detectors in high schools

_____

_____

_____

10. Placing strict limits on the number of immigrants who can enter the United States

_____

_____

_____

EXERCISE 3: WRITING PAPERS – PARAGRAPH ORGANIZATION

CORRESPONDS TO SECTION 4C IN *THE NEW MCGRAW-HILL HANDBOOK* AND SECTION 6C IN *A WRITER'S RESOURCE*

Instructions: Read the paragraphs below. Then answer the questions that follow them. Write your answer to each question in the space to the right.

(1) I went to college to improve my career chances, and now I am a college graduate who has yet to find a job. (2) I got married to share my life with someone. (3) However, my wife's job requires that she travel all over the country most of the year. (4) I am the embodiment of the French aphorism "The more things change, the more they stay the same." (5) I studied hard, chose a wonderful mate, and am now living alone most of the time and jobless in Chicago.

1. What is the topic sentence of this paragraph?   _____

2. Which of the paragraph's five sentences might be removed?   _____

3. Which sentence would make the best concluding sentence?   _____

(1) The drama of real life equals anything movie director Francis Ford Coppola can put on film. (2) The assassination of Anwar Sadat of Egypt on worldwide television surpassed the brutality of the execution segment of *The Godfather*. (3) The bombing of Iraq and burning of Kuwaiti oil fields were as hellish as scenes from Coppola's *Apocalypse Now*. (4) We had the chance to witness both parties to Sadat's murder, both the victim and his killers. (5) Wiretap scenes in *The Conversation* pale in comparison to watching the real thing: FBI videotapes of Mayor Marion Barry smoking crack in a Washington, D.C., hotel room. (6) Indeed, many people claim that real life is stranger than fiction.

4. What is the topic sentence of this paragraph?   _____

5. Which sentence does not relate to the topic sentence?   _____

6. Which sentence would make the best concluding sentence?   _____

(1) Readers interested in the American Civil War will be satisfied with the wealth of available literature. (2) Bruce Catton, Shelby Foote, and James McPherson, among many other scholars, have written extensively on this great conflict. (3) At stake were both the concept of union and the abolition of slavery in this country. (4) These writers show that many complex political issues and personal tragedies were involved in the Civil War. (5) Battlefields have been preserved as national historic sites. (6) Ken Burns's study of this period was the highest-rated public television documentary in broadcast history.

7. What is the topic sentence of this paragraph?   _____

8. Which sentence does not relate to the topic sentence?   _____

9. Which sentence would make the best concluding sentence? _____

(1) Big Sur, on the sparkling Pacific Coast, and the expansive Mojave Desert, where few living things can survive, are worth seeing. (2) The bottomless Grand Canyon is visited by more than a million people each year. (3) Indeed, a tour of the United States offers the vacationer countless memorable images to last a lifetime. (4) The constructed canyons of New York City are startling and have been the setting of many a motion picture. (5) New York also offers many fine restaurants. (6) The architecture of Washington, D.C., is majestic. (7) Even though its crime rate is among the highest in the nation, this city is a wonderful place to visit. (8) It is a delight to visit man-made structures and natural phenomena in this country.

10. What is the topic sentence of this paragraph? _____

11. Which two sentences do not relate to the topic sentence? _____

12. Which sentence would make the best concluding sentence? _____

(1) In 1543, Nicholas Copernicus, a Polish astronomer and mathematician, published *On the Revolutions of the Heavenly Bodies*. (2) In this work, Copernicus argued that the sun was the center of our solar system. (3) Copernicus's theory revolutionized astronomy and cosmology, the study of the structure of the universe. (4) His arguments contradicted the age-old belief postulated by the Greek thinker Ptolemy, who, in the *Almagest*, had claimed that the sun, the stars, and the other planets revolved around the earth. (5) There were several Egyptian rulers called Ptolemy, but Ptolemy the astronomer never ruled Egypt. (6) Galileo, an Italian scientist, proved Copernicus right and Ptolemy wrong. (7) The Copernican theory, first developed by Copernicus and proven by Galileo, is the basis of modern-day astronomy. (8) Galileo developed the telescope, which helped him observe several phenomena that show that the planets revolve around the sun and that heavenly bodies don't move in perfect circles as was once thought. (9) Galileo also discovered sun spots.

13. What is the topic sentence of this paragraph? _____

14. Which two sentences do not relate to the topic sentence? _____

15. Which sentence would make the best concluding sentence? _____

14

EXERCISE 4: WRITING PAPERS – PARAGRAPH ORGANIZATION

CORRESPONDS TO SECTION 4C IN *THE NEW MCGRAW-HILL HANDBOOK* AND SECTION 6C IN *A WRITER'S RESOURCE*

Instructions: Read the paragraphs below. Then answer the questions that follow them. Write your answer to each question in the space to the right.

(1) Prenatal health care is important. (2) In the first trimester of her pregnancy, a woman should see her physician at least once a month. (3) During the first monthly visit, her personal and family health histories are taken. (4) The obstetrician evaluates the woman's blood pressure, pulse, weight, and other important health indicators. (5) Urine and blood samples are also collected. (6) The physician may even let the expectant mother listen to the baby's heart. (7) The doctor explains that the fetus's heart beats twice as fast as hers does. (8) Tests for AIDS, anemia, and other dangerous diseases are performed. (9) The doctor also checks for venereal diseases such as gonorrhea.

1. In which sentences does the author of this paragraph use synonyms for "obstetrician"?

2. In which sentences does the author repeat ideas?

3. In which sentences does the author use linking pronouns?

4. What word in sentence 6 helps maintain coherence?

5. In which sentences does the author use transitions?

(1) When my father was ten years old, his parents died, and he had to leave Russia. (2) He moved to his grandparents' farm, which happened to be in Poland at the time. (3) My father worked in Poland for seven long years. (4) He and his family tilled the soil and cared for the animals at least twelve hours a day. (5) Then, he met a man who was hiring workers for the Danzig shipyards. (6) After working in Danzig for two years, my father got a job on a steamer. (7) It was his work on that ship that first allowed him to visit America. (8) He immigrated to the United States shortly thereafter.

6. In which sentences does the author of this paragraph use synonyms

7. In which sentences does the author repeat words or ideas?

8. In which sentences does the author use linking pronouns?

9. What word in sentence 7 helps maintain coherence?

10. In which sentences does the author use transitions?

15

EXERCISE 5: RESEARCH AND DOCUMENTATION – USING THE LIBRARY

**CORRESPONDS TO SECTION 16A IN *THE NEW MCGRAW-HILL HANDBOOK*
AND SECTION 19A IN *A WRITER'S RESOURCE***

USING CATALYST	www.mhhe.com/nmhh www.mhhe.com/awr
For more information and links to library resources, go to Research > Using the Library	

Instructions: Below is a typical entry from an electronic catalog found in a college library. Read it carefully, and then answer the questions that follow. Write the letter of the correct answer in the space to the right of each question.

AUTHOR(s):   Hancock, Graham.
    TITLE(s):   The message of the Sphinx: a quest for the hidden legacy of mankind
              Graham Hancock, Robert Bauval.
              1st American ed.

              New York: Crown Publishers, c1996
              362 p., [16] p. of plates: ill., maps; 25cm.
              Includes bibliographical references (p. [345]-349) and index.

Example: What is the complete title of the book described in this entry?

  a. The Crown
  b. The Message of the Sphinx
  c. The Message of the Sphinx: A Quest for the Hidden Legacy of Mankind
  d. Can't tell

                                c

1. Where was this book published?   _____

    a. Cairo
    b. Hancock, NY
    c. New York City
    d. Can't tell

2. Who is the publisher?   _____

    a. Crown
    b. Sphinx
    c. Pyramid Press
    d. Can't tell

3. Who is (are) the author(s) of this book? _____

    a. Graham Hancock
    b. Robert Bauval
    c. Graham Hancock and Robert Bauval
    d. Can't tell

4. When was this book published? _____

    a. 1996
    b. 1997
    c. 1962
    d. Can't tell

Instructions: Below is a typical entry from the *Reader's Guide to Periodical Literature*. Read it carefully, and then answer the questions that follow. Write the letter of the correct answer in the space to the right of each question.

PYRAMIDS

Egypt

Age of the pyramids: Egypt's Old Kingdom. D. Roberts. il.supp (folded map) map
National Geographic v187 p2-31+ Ja '95

---

5. Who is the author of this article? _____

    a. Robert D. Kingdom
    b. Egypt's Old Kingdom
    c. D. Roberts
    d. Can't tell

6. What is the article's subtitle? _____

    a. Age of the Pyramids
    b. Egypt's Old Kingdom
    c. *National Geographic*
    d. Can't tell

7. In what periodical is the article found? _____

    a. Age of the Pyramids
    b. Folded Map
    c. *National Geographic*
    d. Can't tell

8. How long is the article? _____

    a. 2 pages

b. 30 pages
c. More than 30 pages
d. Can't tell

9. In what periodical, if any, did this article appear before appearing in the periodical listed here?

         _____

    a. *Science*
    b. *National Geographic*
    c. *Archaeology Today*
    d. Can't tell

10. In what volume of the periodical does the article appear?

         _____

    a. 95
    b. 187
    c. 2-31
    d. Can't tell

Instructions: Below is a typical entry from *Wilson Humanities Abstracts*, an electronic database. Read the entry carefully, and then answer the questions that follow. Write the letter of the correct answer in the space to the right of each question.

AUTHOR: Stocks, Denys A.
   TITLE: Making stone vessels in ancient Mesopotamia and Egypt
  SOURCE: Antiquity (ISSN:0003-598X) v 67 p 596-603 September '93
CONTAINS: bibliography; illustration(s)

SUBJECTS COVERED:
Drilling and boring
Experimental archaeology
Mesopotamia/Antiquities

---

11. What is the title of the periodical listed in this entry?

         _____

    a. Drilling and Boring
    b. Making Stone Vessels
    c. Antiquity
    d. Can't tell

12. Who is(are) the author(s) of the article?

         _____

    a. Denys A. Stocks
    b. Denys and Stocks
    c. A. Denys Stocks
    d. Can't tell

13. How long is the article? _____

    a. 93 pages
    b. 8 pages
    c. 67 pages
    d. Can't tell

14. In what volume of the periodical does the article appear? _____

    a. 93
    b. 67
    c. 598
    d. Can't tell

15. Which of the following subjects would most likely **not** be discussed in the article?

_____

    a. Archaeological methods
    b. Mummification
    c. Excavations
    d. Pottery in antiquity

Instructions: Below is a typical entry from *ProQuest,* an electronic database. Read the entry carefully, and then answer the questions that follow. Write the letter of the correct answer in the space to the right of each question.

Access No: 02690864 ProQuest Periodical Abstracts
Title: Video - Ancient Mysteries-New Investigations of the Unsolved: The Great Pyramid
Reviewers: Beauregard, Sue-Ellen
Journal: Booklist [PBKL] ISSN: 0006-7385 Jrnl Group: Academic
         Vol: 92 Iss 11 Date: Feb 1, 1996 p: 943
         Type: Video Review   Length: Short
Subjects: Video recordings; Egyptian civilization; Investigations; Archaeology;
         Historic buildings & sites
Abstract: Favorable video review

---

16. What type of article does this entry describe? _____

    a. Listing of books
    b. Explanation of how the pyramids were built
    c. Explanation of new investigations of the Great Pyramid
    d. Video review

17. When was the article published? _____

    a. 1992
    b. 1996
    c. 1943
    d. Can't tell

18. What is the title of the article? _____

    a. ProQuest
    b. Periodical Abstracts
    c. Video - Ancient Mysteries-New Investigations of the Unsolved: The Great Pyramid
    d. Can't tell

19. In what journal does the article appear? _____

    a. *ProQuest*
    b. *Booklist*
    c. *Periodical Abstracts*
    d. Can't tell

20. How long is the article? _____

    a. 1 page
    b. 92 pages
    c. 11 pages
    d. Can't tell

EXERCISE 6: RESEARCH AND DOCUMENTATION – TAKING NOTES

CORRESPONDS TO SECTION 21B IN *THE NEW MCGRAW-HILL* HANDBOOK AND SECTION 23B IN *A WRITER'S RESOURCE*

USING CATALYST	www.mhhe.com/nmhh www.mhhe.com/awr
For more information and interactive exercises, go to **Research > Research Techniques** **Research > Avoiding Plagiarism > Summarize/Paraphrase** **Research > Avoiding Plagiarism > Using Quotations**	

Instructions: Read the following direct quotations; then decide which of the three statements that follow each quotation summarizes it best. Write the letter of the correct answer in the space at the right.

> 1. *Personally and politically, Bill Clinton's first thirteen months as president were as tumultuous as the thirteen months he spent campaigning, except that the revelations about his draft-dodging and his experiments with marijuana while a student were replaced by revelations about his and his wife's political and financial dealings while he was governor.*
>
> Meredith L. Oakley, <u>On the Make: The Rise of Bill Clinton</u>

    a. Early in his first term in the White House, Bill Clinton faced as many questions about his character as he did during the presidential campaign.

    b. Personally and politically, the first several months of Bill Clinton's first term were as filled with revelations about his personal life as was the presidential campaign.

    c. Bill Clinton faced a lot of accusations about his personal life in his first year in the White House.

                                       _____

> 2. *From psychiatry, criticism spread to medicine at large. It had long been known that medical care, especially when compared with the environment or social behavior, has relatively modest effect on mortality rates. Nonetheless, the idea that Americans were getting a diminishing return from their increasing investment in medical care hit with the force of a thunderclap in the mid-1970s.*
>
> Paul Starr, <u>The Struggle for Medical Care</u>

    a. In the 1970s, psychiatry was criticized for not helping enough people.

b. Most economists know that medical care is not a good financial expenditure.

c. In the 1970s, Americans suddenly realized that spending a lot of money on health care was not necessarily going to improve the population's long-term health.

_____

3. *You can usually blame a bad essay on a bad beginning. If your essay falls apart, it probably has no primary idea to hold it together. "What's the big idea?" we used to ask. The phrase will serve as a reminder that you must find the "big idea" behind your several smaller thoughts and musings before you start to write.*

Sheridan Baker, <u>The Practical Stylist</u>

a. Good writing begins with a clear notion of the central idea you want to defend or explain.

b. Try to determine the "big idea" behind your writing, for without a primary idea behind your essay, it will soon fall apart.

c. Good writing demands excellent organization skills based on an understanding of the various ideas you want to explain in your essay.

_____

4. *Thirteen's no age at all. Thirteen is nothing.*
   It is not wit, or powder on the face,
   Or Wednesday matinees, or misses' clothing,
   Or intellect or grace.

Phyllis McGinley, "Portrait of a Girl with a Comic Book"

a. At the beginning of her teenage years, a girl feels awkward and out of place.

b. Being a teenager can be difficult.

c. Intellect and grace are not what we ought to expect from thirteen-year-olds.

_____

5. *It is commonly believed by many journalists and politicians that the homeless of America are, in large part, former patients of large mental hospitals who were deinstitutionalized in the 1970s—the consequence, it is sometimes said, of misguided liberal opinion, which favored the treatment of such people in community-based centers.*

Jonathan Kozol, "Distancing the Homeless"

a. Many people believe that, for the most part, the homeless are former patients of mental hospitals who were released because the liberals believed that they would be treated better in community-based centers.

b. Many influential people argue that homelessness has increased since the 1970s because of a decision to remove the mentally ill from hospitals and place them in residential neighborhoods.

c. People in government and the media are contributing to the homelessness problem because they don't understand the real causes of homelessness.

_____

EXERCISE 7: RESEARCH AND DOCUMENTATION – WORKING WITH SOURCES AND AVOIDING PLAGIARISM

CORRESPONDS TO SECTION 21 IN *THE NEW MCGRAW-HILL HANDBOOK* AND SECTION 23 IN *A WRITER'S RESOURCE*

USING CATALYST	www.mhhe.com/nmhh www.mhhe.com/awr
For help with creating a bibliography, go to **Research > Bibliomaker** **For more information and interactive exercises, go to** **Research > Research Techniques** **Research > Avoiding Plagiarism > Summarize/Paraphrase** **Research > Avoiding Plagiarism > Using Quotations** **Research > Avoiding Plagiarism > Using Sources Accurately**	

Instructions: Read the following excerpt; then read the sample citations of the excerpt. Determine which sample cites the excerpt accurately, correctly, and appropriately. Write the letter of the correct citation in the space to the right.

---

1. *From psychiatry criticism spread to medicine at large. It had long been known that medical care, especially when compared with the environment or social behavior, has relatively modest effect on mortality rates. Nonetheless, the idea that Americans were getting a diminishing return from their increasing investment in medical care hit with the force of a thunderclap in the mid-1970s. It suddenly struck intellectuals and policy makers of diverse persuasions that this was the answer to those who constantly wished to expand access to medical care. "The marginal value of one—or one billion—dollars spent on medical care will be close to zero in improving health," wrote the neoconservative Aaron Wildavsky in a clever essay that gave the title* Doing Better and Feeling Worse *to an influential volume on health care sponsored by the Rockefeller Foundation (409).*

Starr, Paul. The Struggle for Medical Care. New York: Basic, 1982.

---

   a. Medicine has come under much criticism because it has only a modest effect on mortality rates.

   b. According to sociologist Paul Starr, medicine came under much criticism in the 1970s because it had only a modest effect on mortality rates.

   c. According to Starr, policy makers of the 1970s had little desire to increase their investment in medical care because they were seeing a diminishing return.

   d. According to Starr, "the force of a thunderclap in the mid-1970s . . . struck intellectuals and policy makers of diverse persuasions."

e. From psychiatry criticism spread to medicine at large. It had long been known that medical care, especially when compared with the environment or social behavior, has relatively modest effect on mortality rates.

f. According to Starr, policy makers of the 1970s had little desire for an "increasing investment in medical care" because they were seeing "a diminishing return" (409).

_____

2. *Women in particular have been discouraged from taking responsibility for solving our own problems, determining our own choices, and taking control of the quality and direction of our own lives. As we learn to relinquish responsibility for the self, we are prone to blame others for failing to fill up our emptiness or provide for our happiness—which is not their job. At the same time, however, we may feel responsible for just about everything that goes on around us. We are quick to be blamed for other people's problems and pain and quick to accept the verdict of guilty (125).*

Lerner, Harriet Goldhor. The Dance of Anger. New York: Harper, 1985.

a. Many women, Lerner says, do not take responsibility for solving problems, making choices, and controlling their own lives. They relinquish responsibility, tending to blame others for failing to make them happy, although that is not their job. At the same time, many women also feel responsible for other people's problems (125).

b. Women should be encouraged to take "responsibility for solving our own problems, determining our own choices, and taking control of the quality and direction of our own lives." Most women today are self-reliant, never "prone to blame others for failing to fill up [their] emptiness or provide for [their] happiness" (Lerner, 125).

c. Lerner maintains that women often fail to accept accountability for solving dilemmas, making choices, or setting goals for themselves, letting others dictate choices in their lives and learning to accuse other people when they are unhappy or unfulfilled. They often feel that other people are responsible for making them contented. Simultaneously, they often accept the responsibility of causing trouble for other people (125).

_____

3. *When Alvarez and company first proposed their radical hypothesis of catastrophic extinction, most paleontologists rejected the idea with ridicule and vehemence. Since then, however, evidence for impact has accumulated to virtual proof—first the initial discovery of iridium at high concentration in strata marking the extinction . . . ; then the finding of shocked quartz in the same sediments . . . ; and finally the apparent "smoking gun" itself, a massive crater of the right age, up to two hundred miles in diameter, off the Yucatan Peninsula in Mexico (163).*

Gould, Stephen Jay. "Jove's Thunderbolts." <u>Dinosaur in a Haystack.</u> New York: Crown, 1995. 159-69.

a. Gould writes that Alvarez's idea of extinction caused by the impact of a meteor was mocked and denounced by other scientists. Since that time, though, many findings have helped to confirm his theory, including the findings of iridium and shocked quartz in certain rocks and the location of the meteor's crater near the coast of Mexico (163).

b. Scientists are quick to spurn and make fun of new ideas, especially the ridiculous idea of a smoking gun extinction (Gould 163).

c. When scientists began finding data of a meteoric impact—iridium and shocked quartz in rocks and the outline of a crater in the Gulf of Mexico—they were more apt to believe Alvarez's theory of catastrophic extinction, according to Gould (159).

———————

4. *I would like to ask God to give me a different nature, so that I don't put everyone's back up. But that can't be done. I've got the nature that has been given to me and I'm sure it can't be bad. I do my very best to please everybody, far more than they'd ever guess. I try to laugh it all off, because I don't want to let them see my trouble* (65).

Frank, Anne. <u>The Diary of a Young Girl.</u> New York: Bantam, 1993.

a. Anne wishes that she could be the kind of person whom other people find easy to get along with. However, she believes that she'll never be able to change her personality. She will always be the way that she is, even though she tries very hard to make others happy (65).

b. Anne knows that she troubles the people around her with her laughing, but they'll never guess (65).

c. Anne writes that she tries to make others happy, but "I've got the nature that has been given to me and I'm sure it can't be bad. I do . . . far more than they'd ever guess."

———————

EXERCISE 8: RESEARCH AND DOCUMENTATION – DOCUMENTING SOURCES

CORRESPONDS TO SECTION 22C IN *THE NEW MCGRAW-HILL HANDBOOK* AND SECTION 24C IN *A WRITER'S RESOURCE*

USING CATALYST	www.mhhe.com/nmhh www.mhhe.com/awr
For help with documenting sources, go to **Research > Avoiding Plagiarism > Citing Sources**	

Instructions: Read the following excerpts from students' research papers. Then answer the questions that follow. Write the letter of the correct answer in the space at the right.

> According to Charles Van Doren, "Roman law was first codified in the Twelve Tables of about 450 BC and remained in daily use in the West until the barbarian invasion of the fifth century AD and in the Eastern Empire until its fall in 1453" (67).

1. Which of the following does the sentence contain? _____

   a. A summary
   b. A paraphrase
   c. A direct quotation

2. Which documentation style does the student use to cite researched material? _____

   a. MLA
   b. APA
   c. Can't tell

> Commenting on the development of the atomic bombs that were dropped on Japan, an important scientist and historian of scientific thought relates that "in a post-war meeting with President Harry Truman, J. Robert Oppenheimer--the scientific director of the Manhattan . . . Project--mournfully commented that scientists had bloody hands; they had now known sin. Afterwards, Truman instructed his aides that he never wished to see Oppenheimer again" (Sagan 284).

3. Which style does the student use to cite researched material? _____

   a. MLA
   b. APA

c. Can't tell

4. Who is the author of the material the student cites in this paragraph? _____

   a. Harry Truman
   b. Carl Sagan
   c. J. Robert Oppenheimer

5. Which of the following does the sentence contain? _____

   a. A summary
   b. A paraphrase
   c. A direct quotation

6. What does the inclusion of the ellipsis (. . .) mean? _____

   a. The student has intentionally removed a word or words from the incorporated material.
   b. The author of the incorporated material intentionally removed a word or words.
   c. The student wanted to create an intentional pause so as to heighten the dramatic effect.

> The extent to which science influences the profession of medicine remains a somewhat controversial subject. For example, K. Hunter (1991) argued forcefully that medicine, despite some popular perceptions to the contrary and "all its reliance on esoteric knowledge and sophisticated technology, is not a science," (p. xvii), even though "the ideal of scientific rationality" (p. xv) is fundamental to our notions of the medical profession.

7. Who is the author of the material the student cites in this paragraph? _____

   a. K. Hunter
   b. Carl Sagan
   c. The student

8. Which of the following does the paragraph contain? _____

   a. A summary
   b. A paraphrase
   c. A direct quotation

9. What does the notation (1991) signify? _____

   a. The year the student wrote this paragraph

b. The year that K. Hunter wrote this text

c. The year that K. Hunter's work was published

10. Which style does the student use to cite researched material?   _____

a. MLA

b. APA

c. Can't tell

11. What does the notation (p. xvii) signify?   _____

a. The page on which the quotation originally appears

b. That this quotation is actually a paraphrase

c. That this quotation was previously published elsewhere

In A Short History of Africa, we learn that:

> After the conquest of the German colony [of South-West Africa] by South African troops during the First World War, the League of Nations' mandate to administer the territory had been given to the South African government. After the Second World War, South Africa, unlike other mandatory powers, refused to recognize that the new United Nations Organization had inherited a supervisory authority over the territory. Thus, South-West Africa, which the United Nations renamed Namibia in 1968, did not become a trusteeship territory to be prepared for self-government. Instead, the South Africans began to incorporate it into their Republic as a fifth province, a process which was complete by 1969. (Oliver & Fage, 1994, p. 234)

---

12. Which style does the student use to cite researched material?   _____

a. MLA

b. APA

c. Can't tell

13. Why is this material indented and not placed within quotation marks? _____

    a. Because it is longer than two sentences
    b. Because it is forty words or longer
    c. Because it is a paraphrase

14. Who wrote the book from which the quotation is taken? _____

    a. Roland Oliver
    b. J. D. Fage
    c. Roland Oliver and J. D. Fage

15. Why are the words *of South-West Africa* in brackets in line one? _____

    a. They were placed there by the authors of the quoted material.
    b. They were inserted by the student for the sake of clarity.
    c. They serve to create emphasis.

EXERCISE 9: RESEARCH AND DOCUMENTATION – MLA STYLE, LIST OF WORKS CITED

CORRESPONDS TO SECTION 24C IN *THE NEW MCGRAW-HILL HANDBOOK* AND SECTION 27 IN *A WRITER'S RESOURCE*

USING CATALYST	**www.mhhe.com/nmhh** **www.mhhe.com/awr**
To download Bibliomaker software for MLA, go to **Research > Bibliomaker**	

Instructions: Each of the following items contains three versions of an entry that could appear in a works-cited page, a listing of sources for a research paper using the Modern Language Association (MLA) style. Choose the correct version, and write its letter on the line to the right.

1. a. Van Doren, Charles. <u>A History of Knowledge</u>. New York: Ballantine, 1991.
   b. Charles Van Doren. <u>A History of Knowledge</u>. New York: Ballantine, 1991.
   c. Van Doren, Charles. (1991). <u>A history of knowledge</u>. New York: Ballantine.

   _____

2. a. Roland Oliver and J. D. Fage. <u>A Short History of Africa</u>. Penguin, 1995.
   b. Oliver, R. and Fage, J. D. (1995). <u>A short history of Africa</u>. Penguin, 1995.
   c. Oliver, Roland, and J. D. Fage. <u>A Short History of Africa</u>. London: Penguin, 1995.

   _____

3. a. William J. Bennet, <u>The De-Valuing of America: The Fight for Our Culture and Our Children</u>. New York, Touchstone, 1992.
   b. Bennet, William J. <u>The De-Valuing of America: The Fight for Our Culture and Our Children</u>. New York: Touchstone, 1992.
   c. Bennet, William J., <u>The De-Valuing of America, The Fight for Our Culture and Our Children.</u> New York, Touchstone, 1992.

   _____

4. a. Kohler, Dayton. "Willa Cather: 1876-1947." <u>College English</u> 9 (1947): 8-18.
   b. Dayton Kohler. "Willa Cather: 1876-1947." <u>College English</u> 9 (1947): 8-18.
   c. Kohler, D. "Willa Cather: 1876-1947." <u>College English</u> 9 (1947): 8-18.

   _____

5. a. Joseph Gies & Frances Gies. <u>Life in a Medieval City</u>. New York: Harper, 1981.
   b. Gies, Joseph and Frances Gies. (1981). <u>Life in a Medieval City</u>. New York: Harper.
   c. Gies, Joseph, and Frances Gies. <u>Life in a Medieval City</u>. New York: Harper, 1981.

EXERCISE 10: RESEARCH AND DOCUMENTATION – APA STYLE, REFERENCES

CORRESPONDS TO SECTION 25B IN *THE NEW MCGRAW-HILL HANDBOOK* AND SECTION 32 IN *A WRITER'S RESOURCE*

USING CATALYST	www.mhhe.com/nmhh www.mhhe.com/awr
To download Bibliomaker software for APA, go to Research > Bibliomaker	

Instructions: Each of the following items contains three versions of an entry that could appear in a references page, a listing of sources for a research paper using the American Psychological Association (APA) style. Choose the correct version, and write its letter on the line to the right.

1. a. Cohen, C. (1997). *Communism, fascism and democracy (3rd ed).* McGraw-Hill, New York.
   b. Cohen, Carl. *Communism, fascism and democracy* (3rd ed). New York: McGraw-Hill, 1997.
   c. Cohen, C. (1997). *Communism, fascism and democracy* (3rd ed.). New York: McGraw-Hill.

   _____

2. a. Sowell, Thomas. *Inside American Education: The Decline, the Deception, the Dogmas.* New York: Free Press, 1993.
   b. Sowell, T. (1993). *Inside American education: The decline, the deception, the dogmas.* New York: Free Press.
   c. Thomas Sowell, (1993). *Inside American education: The decline, the deception, the dogmas.* The Free Press: New York.

   _____

3. a. Rees, M. J. (1990, November). "Black holes in galactic centers." *Scientific American*, pp. 56-66.
   b. Rees, M. J. (1990, November). Black holes in galactic centers. *Scientific American*, 56-66.
   c. Rees, M. J. (1990, November). Black Holes in Galactic Centers. *Scientific American*, pp. 56-66.

   _____

4. a. E. Lane, (1992, November 20). Black hole snapshot: Scientists think that's what Hubble photo may be. *Newsday,* page 7.
   b. Lane, E. Black hole snapshot: Scientists think that's what Hubble photo may be. *Newsday*, (1992, November 20), p. 7.
   c. Lane, E. (1992, November 20). Black hole snapshot: Scientists think that's what Hubble photo may be. *Newsday*, p. 7.

———

5. a. Thomas, Cal. (1993). *The Things That Matter Most.* New York: HarperCollins.
   b. Thomas, C. (1993). *The Things That Matter Most.* New York: HarperCollins.
   c. Thomas, C. (1993). *The things that matter most.* New York: HarperCollins.

———

EXERCISE 11: GRAMMAR REVIEW – THE PARTS OF SPEECH

CORRESPONDS TO SECTION 30 IN *THE NEW MCGRAW-HILL HANDBOOK* AND SECTION 69 IN *A WRITER'S RESOURCE*

USING CATALYST	www.mhhe.com/nmhh www.mhhe.com/awr
For more information and exercises on parts of speech, go to Editing > Parts of Speech For more information and exercises on verbs, go to Editing > Verbs and Verbals For more information and exercises on pronouns, go to Editing > Pronouns For more information and exercises on adjectives and adverbs, go to Editing > Adjectives and Adverbs	

Instructions: The following items ask you to find various parts of speech or parts of a sentence. Write your answer(s) in the space(s) to the right.

EXAMPLE

Find a noun: *clock*

The alarm clock rang loudly.

---

1. **Find a noun:**   _____

   The rain fell hard.

2. **Find two nouns:**   _____   _____

   Jealousy is a silly emotion.

3. **Find two nouns:**   _____   _____

   The mountains of Tennessee are beautiful.

35

4. **Find a pronoun:** _____

   Although Galileo didn't invent the telescope, he greatly improved it.

5. **Find a pronoun:** _____

   His photographs are beautiful.

6. **Find two pronouns:** _____   _____

   Whenever they come to town, we meet for lunch.

7. **Find two pronouns:** _____   _____

   The woman with whom I spoke is Greek.

8. **Find an adjective:** _____

   Sparta is located in southern Greece.

9. **Find an adjective:** _____

   Science was my favorite subject.

10. **Find two adjectives:** _____   _____

    The jade plant grew quickly and soon dominated the tiny room.

11. **Find an adverb:** _____

    The mahogany desk was extremely cluttered.

12. **Find an adverb:** _____

    Economics is a very interesting subject.

13. **Find two adverbs:** _____   _____

    The children suffered terribly when their parents died suddenly.

14. **Find two adverbs:** _____ _____

John Wayne has long been a very popular American actor.

15. **Find a verb:** _____

The Roman Republic emerged in the sixth century BC.

16. **Find a verb:** _____

The Turks won the battle.

17. **Find two verbs:** _____ _____

They heard the noise but ignored it.

18. **Find two verbs:** _____ _____

Although Jefferson opposed political parties, he established the party system.

19. **Find a conjunction:** _____

In 1953 James D. Watson and Francis H. C. Crick identified the double helix as the basic structure of DNA.

20. **Find a conjunction:** _____

Because she loved her brother, she knew he could do no wrong.

21. **Find a conjunction:** _____

Roberto had been in battle but had not been wounded.

22. **Find a preposition:** _____

Shenandoah National Park is in Virginia.

23. **Find a preposition:** _____

Everyone went to church.

24. **Find a preposition:** _____

They ran around the corner.

25. **Find a preposition:** _____

Henry James became a British subject in 1916.

26. **Find an article:** _____

Several of Aristotle's most important works were rediscovered in the Middle Ages.

27. **Find an article:** _____

I needed to buy an umbrella.

28. **Find an article:** _____

We were afraid of the large dog.

29. **Find the subject of the sentence:** _____

Religion is her consolation.

30. **Find the subject of the sentence:** _____

Isaac Newton was born in 1642, the year Galileo died.

EXERCISE 12: GRAMMAR REVIEW – VERBS

CORRESPONDS TO SECTION 30A IN *THE NEW MCGRAW-HILL HANDBOOK* AND SECTION 69A IN *A WRITER'S RESOURCE*

USING CATALYST	www.mhhe.com/nmhh www.mhhe.com/awr
For more information and exercises on verbs, go to Editing > Verbs and Verbals	

Instructions: Do the sentences below need helping or linking verbs? If so, write an appropriate verb in the space to the right of each sentence. If not, write *C* in the space.

EXAMPLE The club meet next Tuesday for the first time.	*will*

1. On her last trip to Akron, the governor seen kissing babies and shaking hands.

      _____

2. I talk to you tomorrow.   _____

3. Toshiro begin his studies at the university next fall.   _____

4. Mardi Gras, a French term meaning "Fat Tuesday," celebrated just before Ash Wednesday in New Orleans.

      _____

5. Last night, wild turkeys running across the field.   _____

6. The train return to the station tomorrow.   _____

7. Tonight, the ocean reflecting the setting sun.   _____

8. The president and the cabinet meeting in the White House right now.

      _____

9. As with all food, the soup taste better if you add garlic.   _____

10. I hope my grandfather come through his heart operation tomorrow.

      _____

EXERCISE 13: GRAMMAR REVIEW – PRONOUNS

CORRESPONDS TO SECTION 30C IN *THE NEW MCGRAW-HILL HANDBOOK* AND SECTION 69C IN *A WRITER'S RESOURCE*

USING CATALYST	www.mhhe.com/nmhh www.mhhe.com/awr
For more information and exercises on pronouns, go to Editing > Pronouns	

Instructions: Each of the items below contains one pronoun. In the space at the right identify that pronoun as personal, relative, indefinite, demonstrative, or reflexive.

EXAMPLE   Epicureans love to enjoy themselves.   *reflexive*

---

1. Alexander Borodin's most famous work, entitled *In the Steppes of Central Asia* (1880), was inspired by his Russian homeland.

   _____

2. No one denies the seriousness of the issue of capital punishment.

   _____

3. "This is the greatest city in the world," the mayoral candidate shouted.

   _____

4. Gustave Flaubert, whose most famous work is *Madame Bovary*, was a nineteenth-century French novelist.

   _____

5. Egotists give themselves great credit for small accomplishments.

   _____

6. The flatworm, which is among the oldest animals, is an invertebrate.

   _____

7. In 1521, the Aztec empire collapsed when its leader, Montezuma, was captured by the Spanish.

   _____

8. The words that Silvio spoke are Portuguese, a Romance language.

_____

9. Sara just met someone from Bucharest, the capital of Rumania.

_____

10. They visited Pikes Peak, in the Front Range of Colorado's Rocky Mountains.

_____

EXERCISE 14: GRAMMAR REVIEW – ADJECTIVES

CORRESPONDS TO SECTION 30D IN *THE NEW MCGRAW-HILL HANDBOOK* AND SECTION 69D IN *A WRITER'S RESOURCE*

USING CATALYST	www.mhhe.com/nmhh www.mhhe.com/awr
For more information and exercises on adjectives, go to Editing > Adjectives and Adverbs	

Instructions: Circle or underline the adjective or adjectives in the items that follow.

> **EXAMPLE**   <u>Exhausted</u>, the swimmer reached for the <u>small</u> boat and climbed aboard.

1. General George Patton (1885-1945) was an expert at tank warfare.

2. Drew Pearson (1897-1969) was among the most influential journalists in America.

3. In Greek mythology, Persephone was the wife of Hades, ruler of the underworld, and daughter of Zeus, the chief deity.

4. Ponchos are cloaks worn in Latin America; they often take a diamond shape.

5. Ivan IV, also known as "Ivan the Terrible," became the first czar of Russia in 1547.

6. Jamaica is an island nation about nine miles from Cuba.

7. The first Spanish colonists came to Jamaica fifteen years after Columbus set foot on the island.

8. Prior to its colonization by Spain, Jamaica had been inhabited by Arawak Indians.

9. In the seventeenth century, British pirates attacked the Spanish fleet off Jamaica.

10. In 1655, the island was seized by the British, who, in turn, were attacked by Maroons, freed slaves who mounted an armed rebellion against the new rulers.

11. From 1490 to 1526, the Jagiellon dynasty ruled the united kingdom of Lithuania and Poland.

12. During the time of Jeremiah, a prophet of the Old Testament, the Hebrews faced many serious troubles. Among them were the capture of Jerusalem by a Babylonian army.

13. Many jumping spiders, which live in regions as diverse as the tropics and the Arctic, are not large.

14. In the corner of my uncle's house sat an old-fashioned Emerson radio.

15. Kabuki is a traditional Japanese dance performed in a stylized manner.

EXERCISE 15: GRAMMAR REVIEW – ADJECTIVES

CORRESPONDS TO SECTION 30D IN *THE NEW MCGRAW-HILL HANDBOOK*
AND SECTION 69D IN *A WRITER'S RESOURCE*

USING CATALYST	www.mhhe.com/nmhh www.mhhe.com/awr

For more information and exercises on adjectives, go to
Editing > Adjectives and Adverbs

Instructions: Rewrite the following sentences in the spaces provided to correct adjective placement problems.

EXAMPLE   The easy black chair was comfortable.

The black easy chair was comfortable.

---

1. The printing earliest technology was xylography, a process that used carved carefully blocks of wood to make an impression on a flat surface.

    _____

    _____

2. Printed early texts produced from blocks of wood have come down to us from eighth-century Japan and China.

    _____

    _____

3. Wooden movable type, begun in China, appeared in Europe during the Middle Ages.

    _____

    _____

4. The German printer Johann Gutenberg (1397-1468) is believed to have invented a technology that gave birth to printing modern methods.

5. Gutenberg used dies to make individual small pieces of type, and he developed a working press that made readable multiple impressions of a text on paper. Gutenberg's invention was supplanted only recently by electronic easier-to-use technology.

_____

_____

_____

_____

6. Sanskrit is an Indo-Aryan ancient language that is part of the Indo-European greater family of languages.

_____

_____

7. Sanskrit was brought to India by the Aryans, who put in place a social and cultural dominant system that lasted for a thousand years.

_____

_____

8. Originating more than four thousand years ago, Sanskrit is the literary classical language of India.

_____

_____

9. Sanskrit is similar to Greek and Latin in that it has a very grammatical complex structure.

_____

_____

10. Today, mostly scholars use Sanskrit, but it is also being employed to write some literary original Indian works.

EXERCISE 16: GRAMMAR REVIEW – PHRASES AND DEPENDENT CLAUSES

CORRESPONDS TO SECTIONS 31D AND 31H IN *THE NEW MCGRAW-HILL HANDBOOK* AND SECTION 71 IN *A WRITER'S RESOURCE*

USING CATALYST	www.mhhe.com/nmhh www.mhhe.com/awr
For information and exercises on phrases and clauses, go to Editing > Phrases and Clauses	

Instructions: The following items ask you to find phrases and clauses. Write your answers on the lines below.

EXAMPLE

Find the phrase:

The Allies invaded Normandy in 1944.

in 1944

---

1. **Find the phrase:**

   Along the dirt road, we saw two small panthers.

   _____

2. **Find the phrase:**

   A bird called to its mate.

   _____

3. **Find the phrase:**

   The lost child, crying loudly for her mother, was hungry and frightened.

   _____

4. **Find the phrase:**

   Washington's small army camped at Valley Forge.

   _____

5. **Find the phrase:**

   After studying Roman law, Benedict of Nursia abandoned the secular world and entered a monastery.

   _____

6. **Find the phrase:**

   Hannibal crossed the Italian Alps with several hundred elephants.

   _____

7. **Find the dependent clause:**

   Buddha, who was born in India, was the founder of one of the world's major religions.

   _____

8. **Find the dependent clause:**

   Mythology is a collection of stories that reflect a culture's beliefs.

   _____

9. **Find the dependent clause:**

   When I left home, I had no money or prospects for a job.

   _____

10. **Find the dependent clause:**

    Perhaps he'll disappear after the circus leaves town.

    _____

11. **Find the dependent clause:**

    Although they originated as social organizations, European trade guilds eventually regulated prices, wages, and production standards.

    _____

12. **Find the dependent clause:**

After the Abbassid Revolution in AD 749, the capital of the Muslim world, which had been in Damascus, was moved to Baghdad.

_____

13. **Find the dependent clause:**

Emperor Frederick I of Germany, who united many small states into a nation, had a red beard and was known as Barbarosa.

_____

14. **Find the dependent clause:**

Beguines, which first appeared in Europe in the twelfth century, were communities of women devoted to charitable works.

_____

15. **Find the main clause:**

Invented in the fifteenth century, watches depended on a spring mechanism for power.

_____

16. **Find the main clause:**

In World War II, Germany, Japan, and Italy were the Axis powers.

_____

17. **Find the main clause:**

Margaret Atwood, who is a Canadian poet and novelist, has written several best sellers.

_____

18. **Find the main clause:**

Hoping to reach the lake by noon, we left early.

_____

19. **Find the main clause:**

One of Rome's greatest emperors, Marcus Aurelius was a stoic philosopher and writer, as well as a military general.

_____

20. **Find the main clause:**

Although Cicero is best remembered as a brilliant writer, he was famous in his day as an orator and a political leader.

_____

EXERCISE 17: EDITING FOR GRAMMAR CONVENTIONS – SENTENCE FRAGMENTS

CORRESPONDS TO SECTION 32 IN *THE NEW MCGRAW-HILL HANDBOOK* AND SECTION 51 IN *A WRITER'S RESOURCE*

USING CATALYST	www.mhhe.com/nmhh www.mhhe.com/awr
For information and exercises on sentence fragments, go to Editing > Sentence Fragments	

Instructions: Circle or underline any fragments you find in the following items. An item may contain more than one fragment.

EXAMPLE

After the war. She moved to England. Studying ancient languages. She became proficient in Greek, Hebrew, and Latin.

---

1. Isaac Newton was born in Britain in 1642. One of the greatest physicists and mathematicians ever. Newton is best remembered for formulating the universal law of gravitation. As well as laws of motion. He also advanced our knowledge of light and optics.

2. The longest river in Italy. The Po River flows from the Alps to the Adriatic Sea. A distance of 405 miles. Its complex delta opens onto the sea in at least 14 different channels. Depositing vast quantities of silt. The city of Ravenna, once on its shores, is now more than six miles from the river.

3. The Etruscans were an ancient civilization that controlled central Italy before the emergence of Rome. A primary influence on Rome. The Etruscans created a sophisticated culture during the seventh and sixth centuries BC. Establishing both a strong army and a fairly large navy. The Etruscans conquered much of Italy before their decline.

4. Susan B. Anthony and Elizabeth Cady Stanton were just two of the women who met in Seneca Falls, New York, in 1848. To demand equal rights for women. Influential to generations of women seeking equality with men. The Seneca Falls Conference insisted that women were the equals of men, and it demanded an equal place in society for women.

5. Between 1846 and 1850 more than a million people in Ireland died as a result of a fungus that destroyed the potato crop in those years. Accidentally transported from America. The fungus first appeared in 1845. Before the blight had run its course, the population of Ireland had fallen twenty-five percent. In addition to the million who died of starvation, more than a million others emigrated to America to escape the great hunger.

6. The smoothest and most efficient highways of the early nineteenth century. Canals are artificial water routes used to transport people and cargo. Canal barges were powered by teams of mules, which would tow them from shore. Later, with the invention of the steam engine. Railroads quickly replaced canals as the fastest and cheapest means of transportation.

7. Born to a family of Irish immigrants in Pennsylvania. Robert Fulton, a friend of Benjamin Franklin. Was a talented painter and designer. Fulton painted miniatures as well as large panoramas. He also worked on the design and development of such things as marble saws, spinning devices, submarines, canal boats, and torpedoes. He is best remembered for producing the first steamboat to operate successfully on the Hudson River in 1809.

8. A well-ordered unit of pike-bearing infantrymen. The Greek hoplite phalanx was the backbone of Alexander the Great's army. The soldiers wore heavy armor, carried large shields, and wielded swords and pikes. Stood closely and protected each other by overlapping their shields in front of them. Entering battle, the soldiers would first attack with the sharp pikes, which could be nine feet long. Then they would finish the battle with their swords.

9. An Italian physicist and astronomer. Galileo Galilei was born in Pisa, Italy, in the sixteenth century. Often credited with the invention of the telescope. Galileo actually only improved on something already invented in Holland. But with his improved telescope Galileo discovered four of Jupiter's moons, explored the surface of the moon, discovered sunspots and the phases of Venus, and mapped the Milky Way.

10. During his lifetime Socrates wrote nothing down. Teaching on the streets and in the open markets of Athens. Socrates believed that true knowledge could be gained only through the process of discussion. His method was to ask questions. Insisting on the ignorance of most people, including himself. Socrates provoked the wrath of many important citizens. At the age of seventy he was tried, convicted, and executed on charges of atheism and corrupting the young.

EXERCISE 18: EDITING FOR GRAMMAR CONVENTIONS – COMMA SPLICES AND RUN-ON SENTENCES

CORRESPONDS TO SECTION 33 IN *THE NEW MCGRAW-HILL HANDBOOK* AND SECTION 52 IN *A WRITER'S RESOURCE*

USING CATALYST	www.mhhe.com/nmhh www.mhhe.com/awr
For information and exercises on comma splices, go to **Editing > Comma Splices** For information and exercises on run-on sentences, go to **Editing > Fused Sentences**	

Instructions: Circle or underline any comma splices or fused sentences (run-ons) you find in the following items. An item may contain more than one error.

EXAMPLE

Although the factory smoke can be seen across the valley, the company spokesperson says it poses no threat. I don't believe him, he has lied before.

---

1. The entire house is filled with stacks of books and newspapers. It's impossible to find anything, the place is a real mess.

2. An important writer from the Age of Enlightenment, Denis Diderot published a thirty-five-volume *Encyclopedia* on the eve of the French Revolution. He wanted to summarize all knowledge, he also wanted to dispel superstition.

3. Born into slavery, Frederick Douglass escaped at the age of twenty. By the time he was twenty-four he was an important spokesperson for the abolition movement he published his famous biography, *Narrative of the Life of Frederick Douglass,* when he was only twenty-seven.

4. Arguing that all laws are instituted to promote happiness for the greatest number of people, Cesare Beccaria was an eighteenth-century Italian legal reformer. He wanted to end capital punishment and torture, he also wanted to rehabilitate prisoners.

5. Romanticism was a nineteenth-century artistic and literary movement that valued emotion over reason intuition was more important to the Romantics than formal, disciplined intellectual thought. Romantics believed in the spontaneous overflow of powerful emotions and feelings. In retrospect, Romanticism can be viewed as a reaction to the Age of Reason, which preceded it.

6. The term *realism* was first used in 1850 to describe a painting by Courbet, the painting was realistic. Realism emerged in the mid-nineteenth century as a response to Romanticism. Realism too was an artistic and literary movement, but unlike Romanticism, which idealized the world, realism tried to show the world as it was.

7. Napoleon's Continental System is a classic example of economic warfare. Napoleon attempted to destroy Britain economically by blocking all of its trade with Europe. The system was a complete failure. Britain developed new markets and expanded trade around the world France was isolated, and its economy suffered due to the loss of English trade.

8. The first electronic, digital computer was built in 1946 at the University of Pennsylvania. Weighing 30 tons and filling a 30- by 50-foot room, this computer needed 18,000 vacuum tubes it used enough electricity to run three 150-kilowatt radio stations.

9. After the invention of the transistor, vacuum tubes were no longer needed in electrical devices like radios, televisions, and computers. Handheld transistor radios quickly replaced the large desktop or stand-alone models in addition, portable televisions entered the market, and computers went from room sized to palm sized.

10. Fans of *The Twilight Zone* will remember Rod Serling's distinct voice and manner. Serling appeared as host at the start of each show, and his voice brought the curtain down on each episode. But Serling did much more than introduce the story he was the creator of the series, and he also wrote many of the shows.

EXERCISE 19: EDITING FOR GRAMMAR CONVENTIONS – SUBJECT-VERB AGREEMENT

CORRESPONDS TO SECTION 34 IN *THE NEW MCGRAW-HILL HANDBOOK* AND SECTION 53 IN *A WRITER'S RESOURCE*

USING CATALYST	www.mhhe.com/nmhh www.mhhe.com/awr
For information and exercises on subject-verb agreement, go to Editing > Subject-Verb Agreement	

Instructions: Write the correct form of the underlined verb on the line to the right. If the original is correct, write *C*. Do not change the tense of the verbs.

EXAMPLE	
The children <u>swims</u> very well.	*swim*

1. The Italians <u>has</u> developed a fine cuisine. _____

2. Robert DeNiro and an international cast star in *1900*, a film that <u>portray</u> life in Italy.

   _____

3. Lou <u>wants</u> to attend your recital. _____

4. The textbook <u>contain</u> 576 pages, and the teacher always assigns his class every page.

   _____

5. Shrimp or chicken <u>are</u> recommended at Roberto's. _____

6. Running every day <u>takes</u> a lot of discipline. _____

7. Watching old movies <u>are</u> one of my favorite pastimes. _____

8. There <u>is</u> too much traffic on these streets. _____

9. There <u>is</u> also too many traffic lights in this town. _____

10. I don't know anyone who <u>come</u> from India. _____

11. Quite a few people <u>uses</u> the running path in the park every day. _____

12. *Hard Times* <u>are</u> one of Dickens's best novels. _____

13. Fiber optics <u>are</u> an increasingly important technology. _____

14. Along the shore <u>stands</u> boaters waiting for the rain to stop. _____

15. Hong Kong and Singapore <u>is</u> former British colonies. _____

16. Joking and laughing <u>helps</u> relieve stress. _____

17. Having a positive outlook often <u>prevent</u> problems associated with stress.

_____

18. The kitchen and the dining room <u>is</u> connected by a long, narrow hallway.

_____

19. Our parents <u>love</u> to visit us on weekends. _____

20. In a small village in Greece <u>lives</u> my in-laws. _____

EXERCISE 20: EDITING FOR GRAMMAR CONVENTIONS – INTERVENING WORDS

CORRESPONDS TO SECTION 34C IN *THE NEW MCGRAW-HILL HANDBOOK* AND SECTION 53B IN *A WRITER'S RESOURCE*

USING CATALYST	www.mhhe.com/nmhh www.mhhe.com/awr

For information and exercises on subject-verb agreement, go to
Editing > Subject-Verb Agreement

Instructions: In the space to the right of each item, write the correct form of the underlined verb. If the form shown is correct, write *C* in the space.

EXAMPLE

The complete subject of a sentence <u>include</u> the subject's modifiers.

includes

---

1. Many experts in mental health <u>opposes</u> the use of medication.

   _____

2. The highlights of that fascinating era <u>appears</u> in this book.

   _____

3. Many merchants in the Mediterranean area <u>closes</u> their shops at midday.

   _____

4. The hardest thing about writing short stories <u>are</u> getting started.

   _____

5. The two public libraries in our city <u>lacks</u> good periodical collections.

   _____

6. The doctors who participate in my health plan <u>holds</u> evening office hours.

   _____

7. The tutors in my college's computerized writing lab <u>knows</u> desktop publishing.

   _____

8. The Moguls, who established an empire in India during the sixteenth century, <u>was</u> originally from Mongolia.

   _____

9. The novels of Toni Morrison, who has taught at Princeton University, <u>has</u> received critical acclaim.

   _____

10. Castles built during the Middle Ages and surrounded by deep, water-filled moats <u>draws</u> hundreds of thousands of tourists each year.

    _____

11. Nigeria, in addition to many other countries on the African continent, <u>produce</u> much of the world's oil.

    _____

12. Korea, along with India, Taiwan, and Hong Kong, <u>have</u> led the surge in economic growth in Asia.

    _____

13. South Africa's apartheid, which once denied civil rights to nonwhites, <u>has</u> been abolished.

    _____

14. Krakow and Prague, eastern European cities that have maintained a distinctively medieval character, <u>attracts</u> many American tourists.

    _____

15. A nest of angry yellow jackets <u>pose</u> a deadly danger to those who are allergic to insect venom.

    _____

EXERCISE 21: EDITING FOR GRAMMAR CONVENTIONS – COMPOUND SUBJECTS

CORRESPONDS TO SECTION 34D IN *THE NEW MCGRAW-HILL HANDBOOK* AND SECTION 53C IN *A WRITER'S RESOURCE*

USING CATALYST	www.mhhe.com/nmhh www.mhhe.com/awr
For information and exercises on subject-verb agreement, go to Editing > Subject-Verb Agreement	

Instructions: In the space to the right of each item, write the correct form of the underlined verb, keeping the tense the same. If the form shown is correct, write *C* in the space.

EXAMPLE   The Norwegians and the Dutch <u>speaks</u> Germanic languages.   *speak*

---

1. Dominique and Francisco <u>dances</u> during the flamenco show.

   _____

2. Peaches and cream <u>have</u> become our favorite dessert.

   _____

3. Billie Holliday's voice and Lester Young's saxophone <u>unites</u> on several famous recordings.

   _____

4. Both an engineer and a conductor <u>is</u> needed to operate a train.   _____

5. The bedroom and the bathroom <u>connects</u> to the living room.   _____

6. Ancient aqueducts and temples still <u>stands</u> as reminders that Rome once ruled the West.

   _____

7. Much of northern Africa and parts of the Middle East <u>were</u> under Roman rule for hundreds of years.

   _____

8. The amphitheater in Pompeii and the Roman forum <u>is</u> evidence of the fact that the Romans were great builders.

   _____

9. The historian and the archeologist <u>has</u> agreed to continue their search for Roman cities and encampments in Syria.

_____

10. Iphigenia and Clytemnestra <u>plays</u> important roles in Greek tragedy.

_____

11. In the *Iliad* of Homer, Agamemnon and his brother Menelaus <u>leads</u> the Greeks against the Trojans.

_____

12. In the *Odyssey*, Odysseus and his soldiers <u>were</u> turned to swine by Circe.

_____

13. Cincinnati, Ohio, and Athens, Georgia, <u>takes</u> their names from ancient history.

_____

14. The most famous general and statesman of Roman times <u>were</u> Julius Caesar.

_____

15. Civil engineering and the rule of law <u>is</u> perhaps Rome's greatest legacies.

_____

EXERCISE 22: EDITING FOR GRAMMAR CONVENTIONS – COMPOUND SUBJECTS

CORRESPONDS TO SECTION 34D IN *THE NEW MCGRAW-HILL HANDBOOK* AND SECTION 53C IN *A WRITER'S RESOURCE*

USING CATALYST	www.mhhe.com/nmhh www.mhhe.com/awr
For information and exercises on subject-verb agreement, go to Editing > Subject-Verb Agreement	

Instructions: In the space to the right of each item, write the correct form of the verb. If the form shown is correct, write *C* in the space.

EXAMPLE Either rain or snow <u>have</u> been predicted.	*has*

1. Neither Julia nor Sylvia <u>buy</u> clothes at full price.   _____

2. Neither Italy nor Greece <u>import</u> olive oil to my country.   _____

3. Neither the lake nor the pool <u>seem</u> to be as cold as it was last year.   _____

4. Either Monday or Tuesday <u>has</u> been declared a holiday.   _____

5. Either poor carpentry or inferior tools <u>was</u> to blame.   _____

6. Either red or crimson <u>is</u> a primary color.   _____

7. Either Virgil or Horace <u>were</u> the greatest Roman poet.   _____

8. In general, neither fish nor chicken <u>contain</u> as much fat as beef.   _____

9. Either alcohol or tobacco <u>is</u> the most commonly used addictive substance.

          _____

10. Neither the sun nor any other star <u>revolve</u> around the earth.

          _____

EXERCISE 23: EDITING FOR GRAMMAR CONVENTIONS – COLLECTIVE NOUNS

CORRESPONDS TO SECTION 34E IN *THE NEW MCGRAW-HILL HANDBOOK* AND SECTION 53D IN *A WRITER'S RESOURCE*

USING CATALYST	www.mhhe.com/nmhh www.mhhe.com/awr
For information and exercises on subject-verb agreement, go to **Editing > Subject-Verb Agreement**	

Instructions: In the space to the right of each item, write the correct form of the underlined verb. If the form shown is correct, write *C* in the space.

EXAMPLE	The army <u>have</u> driven deep into enemy territory.	*has*

1. The faculty at our college <u>hold</u> many doctorates.   _____

2. The family <u>have</u> all agreed to travel by train.   _____

3. When Pavarotti sang at La Scala in Milan, the audience <u>were</u> enthusiastic.

   _____

4. The government of the United States <u>contain</u> three branches: the executive, the legislative, and the judicial.

   _____

5. A commercial airliner's crew <u>are</u> responsible for the passengers' safety and comfort.

   _____

6. The city council <u>decide</u> whether to increase traffic fines.   _____

7. The union that represents many clothing workers in the United States <u>are</u> called the International Ladies Garment Workers Union.

   _____

8. In the film, a group of children begging for alms <u>approaches</u> the UNESCO relief team.

   _____

9. NATO, a military organization founded after World War II, <u>is</u> being expanded.

_____

10. A majority of Americans <u>thinks</u> that the federal government has gotten too big.

_____

11. The Union of Soviet Socialist Republics <u>are</u> no longer in existence.   _____

12. The League of Women Voters <u>sponsor</u> presidential debates.   _____

13. The Congress of Racial Equality (CORE) <u>is</u> a civil rights organization that tries to improve the lives of minorities.

_____

14. Ten million dollars <u>were</u> the total amount saved by the governor's budget cuts.

_____

15. The United States Senate, which has one hundred members, <u>create</u> legislation that is also considered by the House of Representatives.

_____

EXERCISE 24: EDITING FOR GRAMMAR CONVENTIONS – INDEFINITE SUBJECTS

CORRESPONDS TO SECTION 34F IN *THE NEW MCGRAW-HILL HANDBOOK* AND SECTION 53E IN *A WRITER'S RESOURCE*

USING CATALYST	www.mhhe.com/nmhh www.mhhe.com/awr
For information and exercises on subject-verb agreement, go to Editing > Subject-Verb Agreement	

Instructions: In the space to the right of each item, write the correct form of the verb. If the form shown is correct, write *C* in the space.

EXAMPLE   Somebody in Dr. Santiago's office always <u>return</u> phone calls.   *returns*

1. In my class, everyone <u>participate</u> in the writing of group projects.   _____

2. Someone I know <u>intends</u> to travel to Victoria Falls in Zimbabwe.   _____

3. Most of the bread is stale; some of it <u>have</u> gotten moldy.   _____

4. None of the fruit <u>is</u> ripe yet.   _____

5. One of the children <u>are</u> sick with the flu.   _____

6. All of the radios are broken; none <u>has</u> been repaired.   _____

7. Anyone <u>knows</u> that Paris is in France.   _____

8. Some parts of the engine <u>have</u> been stolen.   _____

9. Nothing <u>seem</u> stranger to me than eating cereal for dinner.   _____

10. Everyone <u>have</u> to pay an entrance fee upon entering the ruins of Pompeii.   _____

11. No one <u>were</u> allowed to touch the ancient Greek pottery on display at the archeological museum in Agrigento, Sicily.   _____

12. Everyone <u>listen</u> intently when Carreras sings.   _____

13. In my family no one <u>play</u> a musical instrument.   _____

14. Everyone <u>see</u> Picasso paintings in a different light.   _____

15. Many <u>tries</u> to climb Mt. Everest, but few succeed.   _____

EXERCISE 25: EDITING FOR GRAMMAR CONVENTIONS – REGULAR AND IRREGULAR VERBS

CORRESPONDS TO SECTION 35A IN *THE NEW MCGRAW-HILL HANDBOOK* AND SECTION 54A IN *A WRITER'S RESOURCE*

USING CATALYST	www.mhhe.com/nmhh www.mhhe.com/awr
For information and exercises on verbs, go to Editing > Verbs and Verbals	

Instructions: Change the underlined verbs to the present tense. Write your answers in the spaces at the right.

EXAMPLE   Miriam <u>slept</u> until 7:00 a.m.   *sleeps*

---

1. The child <u>awoke</u> at the sound of her father's singing.   _____

2. John <u>was</u> a mathematics teacher at the local high school.   _____

3. The rain <u>beat</u> on the tin roof of the old house.   _____

4. Running <u>became</u> easier after the first two miles.   _____

5. The fairy tale <u>began</u> with "Once upon a time. . . ."   _____

Instructions: Change the underlined verbs to the past tense. Write your answers in the spaces at the right.

EXAMPLE   Miriam <u>sleeps</u> until 7:00 a.m.   *slept*

---

6. The flowers and trees <u>bend</u> in the wind.   _____

7. Mosquitoes <u>bite</u> the unsuspecting victims.   _____

8. The train whistle <u>will</u> <u>blow</u> at supper time.   _____

9. My heart <u>breaks</u> at seeing that child in rags.   _____

66

10. On occasion, Lyle <u>brings</u> his iguana to class. _____

11. Sally <u>dreams</u> of winning the lottery. _____

12. She <u>deals</u> the cards without looking at them. _____

13. The construction worker <u>wears</u> a helmet at all times. _____

14. The bailiff <u>will</u> <u>swear</u> in the jury. _____

15. I <u>take</u> my suit to the cleaners. _____

EXERCISE 26: EDITING FOR GRAMMAR CONVENTIONS – VERB FORMS, THE *-D* or *-ED* ENDINGS

CORRESPONDS TO SECTION 35E IN *THE NEW MCGRAW-HILL HANDBOOK* AND SECTION 54D IN *A WRITER'S RESOURCE*

USING CATALYST	www.mhhe.com/nmhh www.mhhe.com/awr
For information and exercises on verbs, go to Editing > Verbs and Verbals	

Instructions: Write the correct form of any participle you find in the following items. Use the spaces at the right to record your answers.

EXAMPLE We were suppose to be at the library at 2:00 p.m.	*supposed*

1. They had ice coffee with their meal.   _____

2. She bought a use coat at the Salvation Army.   _____

3. The students look bore.   _____

4. My aunt is not prejudice.   _____

5. Raise in Oregon, Belinda loved the outdoors.   _____

6. The customer ask where she could find the shoe department.

    _____

7. Your parents should be use to his strange ways.   _____

8. The students were use to getting extra homework over the weekend.

    _____

9. The driver was confuse about which direction to go.   _____

10. She had a mix expression on her face when she heard the news.   _____

EXERCISE 27: EDITING FOR GRAMMAR CONVENTIONS – VERB TENSES

CORRESPONDS TO SECTIONS 35G, 35H IN *THE NEW MCGRAW-HILL HANDBOOK* AND SECTIONS 54F, 54G IN *A WRITER'S RESOURCE*

USING CATALYST	www.mhhe.com/nmhh www.mhhe.com/awr
For information and exercises on verbs, go to Editing > Verbs and Verbals	

Instructions: Write the correct form of the underlined verb in the space at the right. If the original form is correct, write *C* in the space.

EXAMPLE My church has runned a bazaar every year.	*has run*

1. Kelly's ancestors had spoke only Gaelic before they came to America.

    _____

2. Prior to Copernicus, many philosophers and scientists had clinged to the notion that the sun moved around the earth.

    _____

3. Silvio had catched malaria during a trip to the tropics.   _____

4. Italian partisans had killed and hung Mussolini by his ankles before the Allies could capture him.

    _____

5. The United States government is digging its own financial grave by failing to control budget deficits.

    _____

6. The doctor had already seen twenty patients today.   _____

7. John tried to put on his slacks, but the manufacturer sewed the pant legs together.

    _____

8. Long before she began studying Greek, she mastered Latin.   _____

9. The potatoes exploded because Aunt Mabel <u>had</u> <u>left</u> them in the oven too long.

_____

10. Before he was fired, my brother <u>has</u> <u>bought</u> a new home.

_____

11. Before they left for vacation, Lisa and Ray <u>have</u> <u>placed</u> all of their valuables in their safe.

_____

12. The dog <u>had</u> <u>had</u> enough to eat this morning.

_____

13. After we got home, we realized that someone <u>broke</u> through the back door.

_____

14. The sailor was brought to the hospital because he <u>has</u> <u>been</u> lost at sea for three weeks.

_____

15. By the time you get home, I <u>be</u> sleeping.

_____

EXERCISE 28: EDITING FOR GRAMMAR CONVENTIONS – SUBJUNCTIVE MOOD

CORRESPONDS TO SECTION 35K IN *THE NEW MCGRAW-HILL HANDBOOK* AND SECTION 54J IN *A WRITER'S RESOURCE*

USING CATALYST	www.mhhe.com/nmhh www.mhhe.com/awr
For information and exercises on verbs, go to Editing > Verbs and Verbals	

Instructions: Are the underlined verbs in the following items correct? If not, write the correct form of the verb in the space to the right. If the verb is correct, write *C* in the space.

EXAMPLE Please <u>moves</u> along!	*move*

1. Lead, follow, or <u>gets</u> out of the way!   _____

2. If the president of the United States <u>was</u> ever considered above the law, our democratic system would be weakened.

    _____

3. My trainer recommends that I <u>avoids</u> jogging until my back feels better.

    _____

4. During the Cuban missile crisis, President Kennedy demanded that the Soviet Union <u>removes</u> its missiles from the Americas.

    _____

5. If Samantha goes to Egypt this summer, she <u>could</u> visit the city of Alexandria.

    _____

6. If I <u>was</u> able to go to St. Petersburg, Russia, I would visit the Hermitage Museum.

    _____

7. If Jonathan reads the chapter on supply and demand, he <u>would</u> pass the economics exam.

    _____

8. If I <u>was</u> living in Poland in 1939, I would surely have been terrified by the coming of the Nazis.

_____

9. If Napoleon <u>did</u> <u>not</u> <u>invade</u> Russia in 1812, he would have remained emperor of the French.

_____

10. If the winter of 1812 <u>was</u> <u>not</u> severe, Napoleon might have won the Russian campaign.

_____

EXERCISE 29: EDITING FOR GRAMMAR CONVENTIONS – PRONOUN-ANTECEDENT AGREEMENT

CORRESPONDS TO SECTION 36K IN *THE NEW MCGRAW-HILL HANDBOOK* AND SECTION 55A IN *A WRITER'S RESOURCE*

USING CATALYST	www.mhhe.com/nmhh www.mhhe.com/awr
For information and exercises on pronouns, go to Editing > Pronouns	

Instructions: In the space to the right of each item, write the correct form of the pronoun. If the form shown is correct, write *C* in the space.

EXAMPLE The cars were having <u>its</u> brakes repaired.	*their*

1. Each of the men took out <u>their</u> camera and snapped a picture of Queen Elizabeth.

   _____

2. Both Cindy and Leslie are cooperative; either can be counted on to lend <u>their</u> help and advice.

   _____

3. The United States Congress meets in <u>its</u> own chamber in the Capitol in Washington.

   _____

4. Neither the United States nor Russia is going to disarm <u>their</u> nuclear arsenal soon.

   _____

5. Both Stalin and Hitler were tyrants; neither served <u>their</u> country well.

   _____

6. Either of the two men was perfectly capable of preparing <u>his</u> own dinner.

   _____

7. Statistics, the study of numerical data, takes <u>their</u> name from a Greek word.

   _____

8. Professional athletics has <u>their</u> drawbacks.   _____

9. After speaking with the father and the son, I knew that neither would take me into <u>their</u> confidence.

                                                                         _____

10. Neither Gloria nor Felice brought a coat with <u>them</u>.   _____

11. When defining economics, some writers have called <u>them</u> an art, not a science.

                                                                         _____

12. I would not believe anything that either of the men told me about <u>themselves</u>.

                                                                         _____

13. The animals were tranquilized; each had a tag attached to <u>its</u> ear.

                                                                         _____

14. The group decided <u>they</u> should not carpool next week.   _____

15. The Committee to Re-Elect the President chose to keep <u>their</u> headquarters in Washington.

                                                                         _____

EXERCISE 30: EDITING FOR GRAMMAR CONVENTIONS – PRONOUN REFERENCE

CORRESPONDS TO SECTION 36P IN *THE NEW MCGRAW-HILL HANDBOOK* AND SECTION 55B IN *A WRITER'S RESOURCE*

USING CATALYST	www.mhhe.com/nmhh www.mhhe.com/awr
For information and exercises on pronouns, go to Editing > Pronouns	

Instructions: Rewrite the following sentences in the spaces provided to correct problems with pronoun reference.

EXAMPLE   The two asteroids collided, which scattered debris for millions of miles.

The collision of the two asteroids scattered debris for millions of miles.

---

1. When Jane and Emily discussed her recent trip to Africa, she told her about a strange flightless bird that was a member of the ostrich family.

    _____

    _____

2. In early 1989, the Berlin Wall was toppled in Germany. This led to Germany's reunification.

    _____

    _____

3. On July 1, 1997, Hong Kong was turned over to the People's Republic of China, which ended Britain's dominion over it.

    _____

    _____

4. In 1941, Japan attacked Pearl Harbor. Because of that, the United States entered World War II.

   _____

   _____

5. In this report, it says that inflation has not proven to be a problem lately, and the Federal Reserve has been able to hold down interest rates.

   _____

   _____

6. In states such as Minnesota, they are used to dealing with cold and snow.

   _____

7. Besides being major producers of automobiles, Korea is also a major producer of appliances and electrical equipment, which signals increased industrial production.

   _____

   _____

8. Iran's carpet industry is highly profitable; they make carpets that hold their value for generations.

   _____

   _____

9. According to the manual, you need to install an AAA battery.

   _____

10. France's grapes are excellent, and they export wines around the world.

   _____

EXERCISE 31: EDITING FOR GRAMMAR CONVENTIONS – PRONOUN CASE

CORRESPONDS TO SECTION 36A IN *THE NEW MCGRAW-HILL HANDBOOK* AND SECTION 55D IN *A WRITER'S RESOURCE*

USING CATALYST	www.mhhe.com/nmhh www.mhhe.com/awr
For information and exercises on pronouns, go to Editing > Pronouns	

Instructions: Write the correct form of the underlined pronoun on the line to the right.

EXAMPLE He sent the letter to Arnold and <u>she</u>.	*her*

1. Miriam supervises Matthew, Gerald, and <u>he</u>. _____

2. There is a bond among Benny, Harry, and <u>we</u>. _____

3. Gordon asked Margaret and <u>she</u> to join them. _____

4. The hoodlums threw rocks at <u>we</u> students. _____

5. <u>Him</u> marrying Gertrude pleased only their parents. _____

6. This vacation will be restful for both <u>we</u> and them. _____

7. Just between you and <u>I</u>, Evelyn is this year's winner. _____

8. Thank goodness! My car was able to pass between the lamppost and <u>they</u>.

   _____

9. She and <u>him</u> have teamed up to study for the exam. _____

10. Emanuel has written a new poem about <u>everyones</u> favorite subject, love.

   _____

11. The caravan made <u>it's</u> way to Rabat, the capital of Morocco. _____

12. <u>They're</u> house was near the Andes Mountains in Chile. _____

13. <u>No ones</u> face seemed familiar to Elena as she looked at the police lineup.

_____

14. <u>Him</u> offering to pay our way to London is very generous.

_____

15. <u>Everyones</u> mind went blank when the professor asked us to explain the Doppler theory.

_____

EXERCISE 32: EDITING FOR GRAMMAR CONVENTIONS – *WHO* VS. *WHOM*

CORRESPONDS TO SECTION 36J IN *THE NEW MCGRAW-HILL HANDBOOK* AND SECTION 55E IN *A WRITER'S RESOURCE*

USING CATALYST	www.mhhe.com/nmhh www.mhhe.com/awr
For information and exercises on pronouns, go to Editing > Pronouns	

Instructions: Write the correct form of the underlined pronoun on the line to the right. If the original form is correct, write *C* on the line.

EXAMPLE   I cannot respect anyone <u>that</u> does not respect my right to disagree.

who

1. Of all of the rulers of ancient Rome, Augustus Caesar is the one <u>who</u> I consider the most interesting.

    _____

2. He is the ruler <u>whom</u> founded the Empire.   _____

3. The artist worked for <u>whomever</u> offered the highest fee.   _____

4. The man <u>whom</u> had driven his car into the back of mine apologized.

    _____

5. Leslie was the one <u>that</u> we elected committee chairperson.   _____

6. You may invite <u>whomever</u> you want.   _____

7. Ricardo, <u>who</u> we met only two weeks ago, has become a close friend.

    _____

8. The Plankos, <u>whom</u> live down the street, saw their daughter off to college just last week.

    _____

9. People <u>whom</u> are honest with themselves find it easy to be honest with others.

    _____

10. The family <u>who's</u> son married my cousin Sally is from Argentina. _____

11. The author <u>whom</u> wrote *Main Street* is Sinclair Lewis. _____

12. Many of the Europeans <u>that</u> settled in Minnesota were Scandinavian.

    _____

13. The Normans, <u>whom</u> were originally known as Norsemen, conquered both England and southern Italy in the eleventh century.

    _____

14. In the Old Testament, Ishmael, <u>whose</u> father was Abraham, was forced from his home by Sarah, Abraham's second wife.

    _____

15. It was Melpomene <u>whom</u> was the Greek muse of tragedy. _____

EXERCISE 33: EDITING FOR GRAMMAR CONVENTIONS – ADVERBS

CORRESPONDS TO SECTION 37D IN *THE NEW MCGRAW-HILL HANDBOOK* AND SECTION 56A IN *A WRITER'S RESOURCE*

USING CATALYST	www.mhhe.com/nmhh www.mhhe.com/awr
For information and exercises on adverbs, go to Editing > Adjectives and Adverbs	

Instructions: Write the correct form of the underlined word or words in the space to the right. If the original is correct, write *C*.

EXAMPLE

The owners of the Titanic <u>reluctant</u> admitted that their ship was not unsinkable.

reluctantly

---

1. The Bill of Rights was <u>actual</u> written apart from the Constitution. _____

2. The music director at my school plays the organ <u>good</u>. _____

3. Celebrity trials are <u>quick</u> becoming popular with TV viewers. _____

4. The car idles less <u>fastly</u> since I tuned its engine. _____

5. The wind blows more <u>harshly</u> during the winter months. _____

6. Marc called for help <u>useless</u>, for no one was around to assist him. _____

7. Having worked in the computer business for years, Lisa <u>confident</u> answered the interviewer's questions.

   _____

8. The man <u>noiseless</u> walked passed the museum's night guard. _____

9. Jennifer <u>reluctant</u> agreed to water her sister's plants. _____

10. <u>Former</u> known as the Sandwich Islands, Hawaii is a popular honeymoon destination.

   _____

11. The United States Clean Air Act (1970) has <u>significant</u> reduced chemical emissions that contribute to acid rain.

    _____

12. Monetarism is an economic belief that controlling a nation's money supply can <u>greatly</u> affect its prosperity.

    _____

13. For some first-time visitors to the tropics, the climate can seem <u>hellish</u>.

    _____

14. Modern Ghana takes its name from a <u>near</u> forgotten African empire established in the sixth century by a people known as the Soninke.

    _____

15. The empire of Ghana had a rich economy, deriving its wealth <u>chiefly</u> from the gold and salt trades.

    _____

EXERCISE 34: EDITING FOR GRAMMAR CONVENTIONS – ADJECTIVES

CORRESPONDS TO SECTION 37B IN *THE NEW MCGRAW-HILL HANDBOOK* AND SECTION 56B IN *A WRITER'S RESOURCE*

USING CATALYST	www.mhhe.com/nmhh www.mhhe.com/awr
For information and exercises on adjectives, go to Editing > Adjectives and Adverbs	

Instructions: Write the correct form of the underlined word or words in the space to the right. If the original is correct, write *C*.

EXAMPLE   The taco did not taste <u>well</u>.   *good*

---

1. The children looked <u>well</u> in their new clothes.   _____

2. The soldiers were able to see for hundreds of yards quite <u>good</u> through the computerized field glasses.

                                                                             _____

3. The citizens of Marakena felt <u>badly</u> about the death of their mayor.

                                                                             _____

4. When my grandmother got home from the hospital, she didn't look <u>worriedly</u>.

                                                                             _____

5. On Sunday morning the freshly baked rolls that my father brought home smelled <u>exquisitely</u>.

                                                                             _____

6. The suspect sounded <u>anxiously</u> when he took the lie-detector test.   _____

7. Because of a severe cold, Ben hasn't smelled very <u>well</u> the last few days.

                                                                             _____

8. I thought that our instructor looked a bit <u>tiredly</u> yesterday.   _____

9. The boxers looked <u>angry</u> at each other during the first round.   _____

10. The pasta primavera, which contains spring vegetables, tasted <u>deliciously</u>.

                                                                             _____

EXERCISE 35: EDITING FOR GRAMMAR CONVENTIONS – COMPARISON

CORRESPONDS TO SECTION 37G IN *THE NEW MCGRAW-HILL HANDBOOK* AND SECTION 56C IN *A WRITER'S RESOURCE*

USING CATALYST	www.mhhe.com/nmhh www.mhhe.com/awr
For information and exercises on adjectives and adverbs, go to Editing > Adjectives and Adverbs	

Instructions: Write the correct form of the underlined word or words in the space at the right. If the original is correct, write *C* in the space.

EXAMPLE Henry likes the beach because it's <u>peacefuler</u> than the city.	*more peaceful*

1. Whenever I see a rainbow, it seems to be <u>more colorfuler</u> than the last one.

    _____

2. Kayla is the <u>more anxious</u> person I have ever met.   _____

3. Today parents of young children have to be <u>more cautiouser</u> than their parents were.

    _____

4. Lenny is <u>most studious</u> than Louise.   _____

5. Working in a department store was the <u>most difficult</u> job I ever had.

    _____

6. Julio's donation was the <u>generousest</u> contribution the church had ever received.

    _____

7. That was the <u>deliciousest</u> chocolate mousse pie I have ever eaten.

    _____

8. Linda's German shepherd is the <u>bigger</u> of her three dogs.   _____

9. In area, Alaska is the <u>larger</u> of all the fifty US states.   _____

10. According to the latest census, Alaska has the <u>most smallest</u> population of any state.

    _____

EDITING EXERCISE 1: EDITING FOR GRAMMAR CONVENTIONS – SENTENCE FRAGMENTS

CORRESPONDS TO SECTION 32 IN *THE NEW MCGRAW-HILL HANDBOOK* AND SECTION 51 IN *A WRITER'S RESOURCE*

Instructions: Rewrite the following paragraphs in the spaces provided to eliminate fragments.

Mecca

Famed as the birthplace of Mohammed, the founder of Islam. The city of Mecca being the holiest city in the Muslim world since the seventh century. Once known as Macoraba. Located in the western part of what is now Saudi Arabia. The Haram, or great mosque, sits in the center of the city. And contains the most holy of holies in the Muslim faith. To this sanctuary, known as the Kaaba, come pilgrims from all over the Islamic world. Mecca's economy being almost totally dependent on these pilgrims.

_____

_____

_____

_____

_____

Early Mexico: Toltec and Aztec

The Toltec civilization flourished in what is now Mexico from about 900 AD to 1200 AD. Building their capital at Tula, north of present-day Mexico City. They created a vast empire. Conquering the Maya. Who had occupied the Yucatan peninsula and parts of Guatemala. However, the Toltec state was not long-lived. After a disastrous civil war, which left Tula in ruins, the Toltec civilization fell into decline. The power vacuum that this development created was eventually filled by the Aztecs. Who crossed into Mexico in about 1300. The Aztecs creating their own empire on the ruins of the Toltec civilization and absorbing much of the Toltec culture. Establishing their capital in Mexico City. The Aztecs ruled the region for more than two hundred years. When they were conquered by the Spanish.

_____

_____

_____

_____

_____

_____

_____

_____

_____

Yin and Yang

Ancient Chinese thought sees the universe composed of two forces or essences: ying and yang. Which are complementary. Ying being the female essence. Yang the male essence. Ying is seen as passive, cool, dark, and submissive. Yang is assertive, warm, bright, and dominant. Ying is associated with mother earth. While yang is associated with the heavens. Furthermore, balance is created when ying and yang are joined. So it is when male and female join to create offspring. Or when the sun (ying) and moon (yang) act in conjunction with each other to mark the passage of day and night.

_____

_____

_____

_____

_____

Bleeding Kansas

"Bleeding Kansas" is the name given to a war between pro-slavery and free-soil settlers. In the territory of Kansas, 1854-1859. In 1854, the United States Congress passed the Kansas-Nebraska Act. Which was sponsored by Stephen A. Douglas. The man remembered as Abraham Lincoln's opponent in the Lincoln-Douglas debates and in the presidential election of 1860. The Kansas-Nebraska Act allowed the two territories to decide for themselves whether they would be slave states or free states. In the past, Congress making that decision.

Intended to stem the tide of violence over the question of the extension of slavery to new territories. The Kansas-Nebraska Act actually made matters worse. Pro-slavery settlers from Missouri flooded into Kansas. As did free-soilers from Northern states. The two sides clashed in violent confrontations. The most significant being the battle at Lawrence, an antislave stronghold. Followed a retaliatory attack by men under the command of abolitionist John Brown of Harpers Ferry fame. The attacks and counterattacks continued for several years until the bloodshed was finally stemmed in 1861. When Kansas was admitted to the Union as a free state.

_____

_____

_____

_____

_____

_____

_____

_____

_____

_____

EDITING EXERCISE 2: EDITING FOR GRAMMAR CONVENTIONS – COMMA SPLICES AND RUN-ON SENTENCES

CORRESPONDS TO SECTION 33 IN *THE NEW MCGRAW-HILL HANDBOOK* AND SECTION 52 IN *A WRITER'S RESOURCE*

Instructions: Rewrite the following paragraphs in the spaces provided to eliminate fused sentences (run-ons) and comma splices.

Polymers

Polymers are substances created by a chemical process in which monomers (small, single molecules) combine to form larger components and generate long chains of molecules. Some polymers are simply combinations of the same kind of monomers, however, copolymers are combinations of at least two different monomers. Polymers are extremely important to life on this planet. Those that occur in nature include cellulose, of which plants are constructed, as well as the materials found in animal parts for example hair and bone contain polymers. An extremely important polymer is nucleic acid, which contains the genetic data in living cells, edible plant starches, which are primary sources of energy for humans and animals, are still another type. Nylon, rayon, and artificial rubber are synthetic or manufactured polymers, all of these products are essential to modern civilization.

_____

_____

_____

_____

_____

_____

_____

_____

_____

The Bronze Age

The Bronze Age is a historical period that came between the Stone Age and the Iron Age, it is characterized by the use of bronze, an alloy of copper and tin, for tools and implements. The use of such tools began in about 5000 BC, by about 1500 BC Bronze Age technology had spread throughout Europe, the Middle East, India, and China. During these 3,500 years, writing and arithmetic were developed so was the plow, the domestication of farm animals, and the use of wheeled carts. Finally, the Bronze Age saw the rise of commerce and manufacturing in towns, the birth of commercial shipping and the creation of many important trades and arts also occurred during this period.

_____

_____

_____

_____

_____

_____

_____

_____

_____

A Bronze Age City

In the early 1990s, Italian archeologists working in Syria found a collection of approximately 15,000 inscribed clay tablets including government, commercial, and religious records these artifacts are thought to comprise the archives of a long-lost empire covering both Syria and Palestine. This hitherto undiscovered Canaanite civilization dates from about 2400 BC, its capital city was called Ebla. The find may cast a great deal of light on biblical history interestingly, many of the place names mentioned in the clay tablets found at Ebla are also found in the Old Testament, including Sinai, Gaza, and Jerusalem place names such as these were probably well known throughout the area, however, names of people, such as Ab-ra-mu (Abraham) and E-sa-um (Esau) also appear in the tablets, as does Is-ra-ilu (Israel) itself. Ebrum, a Canaanite hero and king, is also mentioned in the tablets, that scholars believe he may be Eber, the man from whom the Hebrews believed they were descended, is perhaps the most intriguing idea that has come from the discovery of this Bronze Age city.

_____

_____

EDITING EXERCISE 3: EDITING FOR GRAMMAR CONVENTIONS – SUBJECT-VERB AGREEMENT

CORRESPONDS TO SECTION 34 IN *THE NEW MCGRAW-HILL HANDBOOK* AND SECTION 53 IN *A WRITER'S RESOURCE*

Instructions: Rewrite the following paragraphs in the spaces provided to eliminate subject-verb agreement problems.

Geometry

Geometry, which is a branch of mathematics, study objects in space. The ancient peoples of the Near East was interested in geometry because it allowed them to survey land, but the name of the subject comes from the Greek words *geo,* which refer to the earth, and *metron,* which have to do with the taking of measurements. Among the founders of geometry are Pythagoras, who lived in the fifth century BC. Euclid, a Greek living in Alexandria, Egypt, during the third century, took the work of earlier mathematicians such as Pythagoras and organized it into his *Elements,* a work that contain his now-famous axioms and common notions. These principles culminated in theorems and has formed the basis for further study in geometry. Euclid's *Elements* were translated from Greek to Arabic in the eighth century AD and from Arabic to English in the twelfth century. Today the principles of geometry has developed far beyond the Euclidean model--which concern itself with flat surfaces (plane geometry) and three-dimensional objects (solid geometry)--to include the study of figures that exists nowhere in nature but is solely the product of abstract thought or of the imagination.

_____

_____

_____

_____

_____

_____

_____

_____

The Zulu People

The Zulu, who make up the largest black ethnic group in South Africa, inhabits the villages and cities of South Africa's province of Kwazulu/Natal, which extend to the Indian Ocean. The Zulu community comprise extended families governed by a patriarch or father figure. Most Zulu are farmers, but some of their men has had to leave the villages to seek work in mines and factories in other parts of South Africa. Typically, everyone in a Zulu family are devoted to each other, and the Zulu even engage in the worship of ancestors, whom they believes can protect them and bring them prosperity and happiness. In fact, when the ghost of someone who have died visit a village, usually in the form of a snake, the Zulu sacrifice a young goat or other small animal in its honor. Anyone who have visited South Africa know why the Zulu has become famous for their music and dances, which they perform during festivals and religious celebrations. In one such ceremony, boys who is passing into manhood undergoes a colorful initiation ritual that recall the days when the Zulu were fierce warriors and controlled much of eastern South Africa. Today, the Inkatha Freedom Party (IFP) are controlled by the Zulu. At first, they opposed the agreement between South Africa's white government and the African National Conference (ANC). More recently, the IFP have participated in free elections. In 1994, in fact, they helped elect a new South African government, which were led by the ANC's Nelson Mandela, the first black president in the country's history.

The Jaguar

The jaguar is easily the largest cat in the Western Hemisphere. This magnificent feline, which is just as strong and fast as any of the great African cats, measure eight and a half feet from nose to tail and weigh up to four hundred pounds. Jaguars cover an expansive range from Texas, Arizona, and New Mexico southward through Mexico, Central America, and South America to northern Argentina. The jaguar has no natural enemies; only humans, and even then only those who are well armed, poses any threat to this great cat. Jaguars live on a diet ranging from small animals and fish to deer and crocodiles, but anyone who have ever lived in an area inhabited by jaguars know too well that they attack farm stock, including pigs, horses, and cattle. Nonetheless, jaguars rarely if ever attack people if not provoked, and no instance of the animal preying on people for food have ever been reported. Nocturnal by nature, jaguars do occasionally hunt and fish during the day. While fishing, the jaguar taps its tail lightly on the surface of the water to lure fish within striking distance. The jaguar is an excellent swimmer and a fast runner. So strong are these cats that a party of tourists in Central America have recently reported seeing a jaguar carrying a cow in its jaws. Finally, because of its strength, agility, and speed, the jaguar is among the few animals that looks down from the treetops and hunts their prey in the relative safety that height and distance provides. As their weight and size attests, jaguars seldom go hungry.

_____

_____

_____

_____

_____

_____

_____

_____

_____

_____

The Bolshoi Company

Founded in 1773, the world-famous Bolshoi Ballet had its roots in a Moscow orphanage that established a dancing school for its children. The company were given the name Bolshoi ("Great" in Russian) when in 1825 it moved to a new theater owned by the Crown. Shortly after that building burned in the 1850s, the theater and the company was reestablished on a larger scale; the new theater had a capacity of more than 2,000 people. Both ballets and operas from all over Europe was staged in this building. Later on, the Soviet government were asked for funds to expand this building. In the 1960s, the Soviets constructed a new home for the Bolshoi Ballet Company, the Kremlin Palace of Congresses, which hold an audience of 6,000. Although Russia has gone through several European wars, two world wars, a devastating revolution, the fall of communism, numerous political purges, and many economic crises since the company's inception, the Bolshoi have survived, its members traveling widely and earning international acclaim for what are now considered by many to be the world's premier ballet company.

_____

_____

_____

_____

_____

_____

_____

_____

_____

_____

EDITING EXERCISE 4: EDITING FOR GRAMMAR CONVENTIONS – PRONOUN-ANTECEDENT AGREEMENT

CORRESPONDS TO SECTIONS 36K–36O IN *THE NEW MCGRAW-HILL HANDBOOK* AND SECTION 55A IN *A WRITER'S RESOURCE*

Instructions: Rewrite the following paragraphs in the spaces provided to eliminate pronoun-antecedent agreement problems. In the process, eliminate any sexist pronouns.

Roquefort: The King of Cheese

A blue cheese made from ewe's milk, Roquefort is one of the oldest known cheeses. In France, where they are made, they are called "the cheese of kings and popes." In fact, Roquefort was a favorite of the emperor Charlemagne in the eighth century. Legend has it that he asked each of his cooks to incorporate the cheese into their favorite dish. The distinctively sharp and tangy Roquefort wheels are produced only in Roquefort, near Toulouse in southern France, where it is aged in limestone caves. The caves are both cool and humid, and its unique atmosphere causes the growth of the fine blue mold which makes the cheese famous. The Italians and the Danes also produce very fine blue cheeses, but neither country's blue cheeses has the unique flavor and reputation of the French variety. Often imitated, Roquefort, as the French would say, has never been duplicated. They have remained, since the time of Charlemagne, among France's greatest treasures.

_____

_____

_____

_____

_____

_____

_____

_____

_____

Jordan

As a modern state, Jordan traces its origins to 1916, when world war and local revolt secured their freedom from the Ottoman Empire, that had controlled the area since the sixteenth century. Jordan, which only gained its full independence in 1946 as the Hashemite Kingdom of Transjordan, took their present name from the Jordan River in 1949. Today, Jordanians are fiercely patriotic and proud of his country. She is a land of high desert and steep, elevated hills, with a fifteen-mile coastline on the Red Sea. Jordan is the home of some of the oldest settled sites in the world. The ancient city of Jericho, the oldest permanent human settlement ever found, is located in their country. Through much of this century, the Hashemite family has governed Jordan, with one of their members, the current King Abdullah II, having ruled the country since 1999.

_____

_____

_____

_____

_____

_____

_____

_____

_____

_____

The Shakers

Of all of the Utopian communities that emerged in America in the 1820s, perhaps the most successful was that of the Shakers. The first Shaker community was started in 1779 by Ann Lee on a small piece of property near Albany, New York. Over the next few decades, they grew, and Shaker converts founded communities in other places. In fact, dozens of Shaker communities sprouted up throughout New England and the Midwest. Each had their own identity, but all followed the same lifestyle and moral code. During the nineteenth century, thousands of people joined the Shaker cause. Anyone who converted to Shakerism had to commit himself to a life of simplicity, celibacy, and hard work. They would become famous for the furniture and other crafts, as well as for many inventions, including the circular saw and the flat broom. Because the Shakers had vowed to be celibate, no one could hope to pass on his lifestyle to his children, nor could they expect to replenish their ranks with their descendants. As a result, the community depended on converts to keep themselves going, but by the 1890s conversions were becoming rare. As a movement, therefore, they continued to decline. By the late 1980s, only twelve known Shakers remained, each of them in his nineties.

_____

_____

_____

_____

_____

_____

_____

_____

_____

_____

_____

EDITING EXERCISE 5: EDITING FOR GRAMMAR CONVENTIONS – PROBLEMS WITH VERBS

CORRESPONDS TO SECTION 35 IN *THE NEW MCGRAW-HILL HANDBOOK* AND SECTION 54 IN *A WRITER'S RESOURCE*

Instructions: Rewrite the following paragraphs in the spaces provided to eliminate problems with verbs or words made from verbs.

Alchemy: Precursor to Modern Chemistry

The Greek philosopher Aristotle, who live during the fourth century BC, taught that all matter could be perfected, thereby giving rise to the pseudoscience of alchemy, the attempt of "perfecting" base metals by turning them into gold. Alchemists clinged to the idea that they might also discover the elixir of life, a substance that could extend human life. Although it reached its height during the Middle Ages, alchemy had began in the Greek city of Alexandria, Egypt, in ancient times. There is evidence that it also is being practiced in China at the same time. Greek and Roman philosophers, including Empedocles (fifth century BC) and the Roman emperor Caligula (first century AD) studied alchemy and, in the process, discovered a number of principles that will eventually point to the rise of chemistry many centuries later. In the third century, for example, the Greek Zosimus experiments with sulfuric acid and discovers many of its properties and capabilities. For four centuries, Arab alchemists experimenting with metals such as gold, arsenic, and sulfur uncover a number of important chemical principles and techniques, which they recorded and publish. This knowledge has came to Europe through Spain, which the Arabs controlled for many centuries. European thinkers such as Roger Bacon, Thomas Aquinas, and Albertus Magnus helped furthering the study of what had became known as chemistry. In the sixteenth century, the Swiss philosopher Paracelsus theorizes that there are one element from which all others springed and that can act as the universal solvent, as a cure for all diseases, and as the philosopher's stone (the substance that will turn base metals into gold). The followers of Paracelsus took two directions: the first develop into legitimate scientists, leading the way to France's Antoine Lavoisier, the founder of modern chemistry. The second group eventually turned alchemy into the study of black magic and sorcery, giving it the image it had retained to this day.

_____

_____

_____

_____

_____

_____

_____

_____

_____

_____

_____

_____

_____

_____

_____

_____

_____

_____

_____

_____

_____

_____

Zululand

Members of a group of people speaking the Nguni languages, the Zulu live in what is now South Africa. With the largest number of that country's indigenous people, the Zulu ethnic group numbers about nine million. In the nineteenth century, they united with other members of the Nguni under a Zulu leader named Shaka, who rule from 1816 to 1828. Shaka extends Zulu control beyond their native lands into the area known as Natal on the Indian Ocean. In 1879, war broke out between the Zulus and the British, who had colonize southern Africa. The Zulu were victorious in several early battles. If the British did not change their tactics and brought in reinforcements, however, they would surely be vanquished. However, the Zulu are eventually defeated, and their country was divided into thirteen separate kingdoms under British control. In 1887, Zululand was officially name a Crown colony of Great Britain. Under apartheid, parts of Zululand have been combined into Kwazulu, a separate black homeland. Apartheid was a political system designed on keeping power and wealth in the hands of whites of denying civil and economic rights to nonwhite South Africans. At the heart of the system was the enforcement of a strict policy of racial segregation. With the abolition of apartheid in 1994, Kwazulu was joined with Natal to form a new province.

_____

_____

_____

_____

_____

_____

_____

_____

_____

_____

The Doppler Effect

A native of Vienna, Austria, Christian Doppler (1803-53) had been a physicist who developed a theory about light waves that drawed upon what was already knew about the movement of sound. Knowed as the Doppler Effect, the theory was first published in a study entitled "Concerning the Coloured Light of Double Stars" (1842). As we move toward a blaring horn, Doppler explains, the sound gets louder and louder; as we move away from the horn, the sound diminishes. This, he argued, can being compared to the way in which light from a star reaches us. As the earth moves closer and closer to the star, its light arrives in shorter and shorter wavelengths (toward the violet end of the spectrum); as the earth moves farther and farther away from the star, its light has arrived in longer and longer wavelengths (toward the red end of the spectrum). Today, Doppler's work had importance in research on the nature of the universe and is especially important to understanding the movement of the stars.

_____

_____

EDITING EXERCISE 6: EDITING FOR GRAMMAR CONVENTIONS –
PROBLEMS WITH PRONOUNS

CORRESPONDS TO SECTION 36 IN *THE NEW MCGRAW-HILL HANDBOOK* AND SECTION 55 IN *A WRITER'S RESOURCE*

Instructions: Rewrite the following paragraphs in the spaces provided to eliminate problems with pronouns.

The Illustrious Curies

Both Marie Skladowska Curie and her daughter, Irene Curie Joliot, make excellent starting points for an argument that women excel in science. Marie Skladowska, whom was born in Warsaw, Poland, in 1867, was a chemist and physicist who's research won her acclaim around the world. In 1895, after she moved to Paris, she married Pierre Curie, another physicist that shared her interest in uranium. Together they discovered radium and polonium, whom she named after the country of her birth. With Henri Becquerel, the man that discovered radioactivity, Marie and Pierre Curie shared the Nobel Prize for physics in 1903. Eight years later, Marie won a second Nobel Prize, this time for chemistry. Thus, she became the first person that had ever won the prize twice. Three years before that, Pierre Curie had begun teaching at the Sorbonne in Paris while continuing to pursue scientific research with his wife. In 1906, however, that ended when he was run over by a large horse-drawn wagon and killed. Of course, Marie became distraught over that, but she vowed to complete that work. Indeed, she took up Pierre's professorship at the Sorbonne (she was the first woman that had ever taught at that university) and continued their research. The Curies had a daughter, Irene, that was as important to the history of science as her parents. In 1935, she won the Nobel Prize for chemistry with her husband, Frederic Joliot.

_____

_____

_____

_____

_____

_____

_____

_____

_____

The Copts

The Copts are a people that claim to be descendants of the ancient Egyptians. They speak a language that has evolved from the language of the people whom were living at the time of the pharaohs. However, unlike the ancient Egyptians, whom employed hieroglyphics to write their language, the Copts use the Greek alphabet along with seven characters taken from an earlier form of Egyptian writing. Egypt was conquered by the Arabs in the seventh century AD. It resulted in Islam becoming the country's dominant religion. However, the early Muslim rulers of Egypt, who have been studied by historians of the Near East, were relatively tolerant of the Copts, whom were Christian. Today there are two Coptic churches: the Coptic Church, which is aligned with Rome, and the Coptic Orthodox Church, which is the main Christian Church in Egypt and which has a closer connection with Greek Orthodoxy. Copts continue to practice their religion, but some Islamic fundamentalists have begun to harass and discriminate against them. That has caused Copts to leave Egypt and immigrate to the United States in increasing numbers.

_____

_____

_____

_____

_____

_____

_____

_____

EDITING EXERCISE 7: EDITING FOR GRAMMAR CONVENTIONS – PROBLEMS WITH ADJECTIVES AND ADVERBS

CORRESPONDS TO SECTION 37 IN *THE NEW MCGRAW-HILL HANDBOOK* AND SECTION 56 IN *A WRITER'S RESOURCE*

Instructions: Rewrite the following paragraphs in the spaces provided to eliminate problems with adjectives and adverbs. Also, eliminate problems with participles, adjectives made from verbs.

Polyphemus

The *Odyssey,* compose more than 2,700 years ago, is the second of the great two epics (heroic long poems) about the Trojan War. History has given the name Homer to the creator of these poems, the first of which is the *Iliad*. These two works are, perhaps, the more well known epics in all of literature. The *Iliad* tells the story of the sack of Troy by Greeks seekin revenge for the stealing of Helen, the wife of King Menelaus, by Paris, a prince of Troy. The *Odyssey* is the story Odysseus, one of the Greek chiefs, and his decade-long, arduous journey home to Ithaca after the destruction of Troy. Experienced many strange adventures and meetin many interesting figures from mythology along the way, Odysseus has become a model for other literary characters who are forced to wander the world searched for family, love, happiness, and the meaning of life itself. Among the more terrifying adventures experience by Odysseus and his men was their meeting with Polyphemus, one of the Cyclops, or one-eye giants, who were the sons of Poseidon, god of the sea, and a sea nymph. After being wash ashore in Sicily, Odysseus and some of his men were captured by Polyphemus, who imprisoned them in his cave by rolling a boulder against the entrance. Each day, the monster vowed to eat two of the intruders alive. Even after having polish off six of the men, Polyphemus still seemed hunger for the young tender flesh of the Greek warriors. Bein the most cleverest of all the Greek commanders, however, Odysseus careful devised a scheme to get his soldiers out of this near impossible predicament. After trickin the monster into drinking too many wine and gettin him complete drunk, Odysseus and his men drove a burning sharp log into the giant's large single eye. Blinding the giant made it possible for the Greeks to escape quick and safe.

_____

_____

_____

_____

_____

_____

_____

_____

_____

_____

_____

Angkor, Cambodia

Cambodia, locate in Southeast Asia, is an ancient beautiful country famous for, among other things, its ornate, vast ceremonial architecture locating at Angkor. Angkor is the site of several capitals of the Khmer Empire, which for centuries rule much of Southeast Asia-- included Cambodia, Thailand, Laos, and Vietnam--quite good. Yasovarman established the first capital at Angkor in the ninth century AD. About three hundred years later, Suryavarman II built a temple complex called Angkor Wat. The most famous tourist site in Cambodia, Angkor Wat still looks relatively well today. It displays the influence of Hinduism, a religion that traveled to Southeast Asia from India. Perhaps one of the world's more larger moats (it is about a mile long on each side), surrounds the complex. Design as a protection from enemies, it provided a formidable obstacle to invaders, intruders, and other unwant visitors. Today, the temple can be reached only after one crosses a long beautiful causeway. Nearby, one can see the city of Anghor Thom, built by Jayavarman VII (1181-1218), which reflects an adherence to Buddhism quite clear. The city once had a population in the hundreds of thousands, but it was abandoned in the fifteenth century. In the years that followed, it became increasing overgrown with jungle, and it fell into ruins. Redisover by the French explorer Henri Mouhot in 1861, Angkor is now visited by archeologists and tourists from around the world. In fact, an internationally effort has been launched only recent to preserve and restore its legacy.

_____

_____

_____

_____

_____

_____

EXERCISE 36: EDITING FOR CLARITY – WORDINESS AND UNNECESSARY REPETITION

CORRESPONDS TO SECTIONS 38A AND 38C IN *THE NEW MCGRAW-HILL HANDBOOK* AND SECTIONS 38A AND 38B IN *A WRITER'S RESOURCE*

USING CATALYST	www.mhhe.com/nmhh www.mhhe.com/awr
For information on and practice eliminating redundancies, go to Editing > Wordiness	

Instructions: Revise the following sentences in the spaces provided to eliminate repetition.

EXAMPLE   She was the oldest sister of the three sisters.

She was the oldest of the three sisters.

---

1. A famous and noteworthy African-American diplomat, Ralph Bunche won the Nobel Prize for Peace in 1950.

   _____

   _____

2. A year earlier than this, in 1949, Bunche negotiated a successful agreement ending the dispute between the Arabs and the Israelis and their struggle over Palestine.

   _____

   _____

3. Bunche served in the US State Department during World War II, and he was instrumental in playing an important role in the San Francisco conference at which preliminary preparations for the formation of the United Nations were being planned.

   _____

   _____

   _____

4. In 1956, Bunche was asked to oversee and supervise the deployment of a United Nations peacekeeping force that was sent to the area of the Suez Canal, which had been invaded by French, British, and Israeli troops.

5. In 1960, he was put in charge of UN forces that were sent to the Congo, which was experiencing a great deal of political unrest at this point in time. Four years later, Bunche used his brilliant genius for negotiations to work out a plan that would cease hostilities between the Greek and Turkish residents of the island of Cyprus, who were battling each other.

_____

_____

_____

6. Animals have to be good at identifying and recognizing their kin and the members of their family.

_____

_____

7. But in some cases they have a contradictory and paradoxical need to blend in.

_____

8. No one wants to be conspicuous or to stand out from the crowd when a predator comes growling into town.

_____

9. Zebras don't have stripes just to identify one another; they have stripes in order to confuse and confound large predatory cats who want to kill them.

_____

_____

10. When attacked and preyed upon, zebras run in every direction and every which way, and the stripes make the predator feel dizzy and woozy.

_____

_____

EXERCISE 37: EDITING FOR CLARITY – WORDY PHRASES

CORRESPONDS TO SECTION 38B IN *THE NEW MCGRAW-HILL HANDBOOK* AND SECTION 38C IN *A WRITER'S RESOURCE*

Instructions: Rewrite the following sentences to make them more direct.

EXAMPLE   Lisa is the kind of person who enjoys the science of biology.

Lisa enjoys biology.

---

1. Both Zena Dohbuti and Gabriella Wecksleva were born in the month of July.

    _____

2. When he was young, Chris Kingsilver was a surveyor who measured land.

    _____

3. Before entering into the study of engineering, Abraham Bieden was a man who split logs and piloted rafts down the river.

    _____

    _____

4. Cecil Rhodes believed that a railway constructed from Cape Town to Cairo would improve transportation and commerce throughout the continent of Africa.

    _____

    _____

5. The geologists conducted an analysis of the mineral deposits that were found in the soil.

    _____

    _____

6. The Food and Drug Administration conducted a test of the new anti-AIDS vaccine.

    _____

7. Although both Washington and Lincoln faced strong opposition during their terms as president, at the present time both men enjoy almost universal respect and admiration.

   _____

   _____

8. It is denied by many archeologists that the lost continent of Atlantis was more than just a myth.

   _____

   _____

9. By 1860 the North and the South could not arrive at an agreement on the future of slavery or of the nation.

   _____

   _____

10. During the month of July, the whole of the southern hemisphere is in the season of winter.

    _____

    _____

EXERCISE 38: EDITING FOR CLARITY – MISSING WORDS

CORRESPONDS TO SECTION 39 IN *THE NEW MCGRAW-HILL HANDBOOK* AND SECTION 39 IN *A WRITER'S RESOURCE*

USING CATALYST	www.mhhe.com/nmhh www.mhhe.com/awr
For information and exercises on missing words, go to Editing > Word Choice	

Instructions: Revise the following sentences in the spaces provided to include necessary words.

EXAMPLE   Maurice kicked his feet and relaxed.

Maurice kicked up his feet and relaxed.

---

1. The professor explained the Etruscans predated the rise of Roman civilization in Italy.

    _____

2. One theory about the coming of the Etruscans to Italy can be traced to Greek historian named Herodotus.

    _____

    _____

3. Herodotus believed the Etruscans, who came to Italy about 3,200 years ago, once lived in Asia Minor.

    _____

    _____

4. They created a civilization more advanced than of any people living in Italy at that time.

    _____

5. The tongue that the Etruscans spoke was strange; it can be likened to no other type language we now know.

_____

_____

Instructions: In these next sentences, include missing words, and replace misspelled words.

6. The class listened too the account of the San Francisco earthquake intently as possible.

_____

_____

7. In fact, the earthquake of 1906 will probably be regarded one of the most devastating natural disasters inn American history, but none of us knew that it had been so destructive.

_____

_____

8. The annihilation, wrought upon a city that was totally unprepared four a major earthquake, was great as can be imagined.

_____

_____

9. Indeed, old San Francisco was nearly obliterated, but the rebirth of the city only a few years later has and always will be one of the most inspiring stories in the history off California.

_____

_____

_____

10. Today, buildings in earthquake zones are constructed with technologies designed two withstand earth tremors; perhaps future earthquakes may not cause tragedies horrible as the one San Francisco's turn-of-the-century inhabitants once suffered.

_____

_____

CORRESPONDS TO SECTION 41C IN *THE NEW MCGRAW-HILL HANDBOOK* AND SECTION 41B IN *A WRITER'S RESOURCE*

Instructions: The following items contain three versions of the same sentence. Write the letter of the correct version on the line to the right.

EXAMPLE

   a. Jenn watched the house and eats all the food.
   b. Jenn watched the house and will eat all the food.
   c. Jenn watched the house and ate all the food.

                                                            c

---

1. a. Fire destroy the village and burned the countryside.
   b. Fire destroyed the village and burned the countryside.
   c. Fire destroyed the village and burns the countryside.

                                             _____

2. a. Monica and Elizabeth could not find Sarah's house; they have taken the wrong road.
   b. Monica and Elizabeth could not find Sarah's house; they take the wrong road.
   c. Monica and Elizabeth could not find Sarah's house; they had taken the wrong road.

                                           _____

3. a. There must be a hundred crows in the field; the corn was what they were eating.
   b. There must have been a hundred crows in the field; they are eating the corn.
   c. There must be a hundred crows in the field; they are eating the corn.

                                           _____

4. a. Ricardo stayed home all afternoon and watched television.
   b. Ricardo is staying home all afternoon and watched television.
   c. Ricardo stayed home all afternoon and is watching television.

                                           _____

5. a. Every time Charlotte has gone to Europe she enjoys eating in expensive restaurants.

b. Every time Charlotte went to Europe she enjoys eating in expensive restaurants.
c. Every time Charlotte goes to Europe she enjoys eating in expensive restaurants.

_____

6. a. When Golriez graduated from the university, she found a job immediately.
   b. When Golriez graduated from the university, she had found a job immediately.
   c. When Golriez graduated from the university, she was finding a job immediately.

_____

7. a. I visited my grandfather yesterday, and I came back before seven o'clock.
   b. I visited my grandfather yesterday, and I come back before seven o'clock.
   c. I visited my grandfather yesterday, and I had come back before seven o'clock.

_____

8. a. As soon as it started raining, everybody left the park.
   b. As soon as it started raining, everybody was leaving the park.
   c. As soon as it started raining, everybody had left the park.

_____

9. a. When Antwan was in college, his major will be chemistry.
   b. When Antwan was in college, his major is chemistry.
   c. When Antwan was in college, his major was chemistry.

_____

10. a. While I was drinking a glass of chocolate milk, the mail carrier will come.
    b. While I was drinking a glass of chocolate milk, the mail carrier came.
    c. While I was drinking a glass of chocolate milk, the mail carrier is coming.

_____

11. a. Maria wanted to start her own business and make a lot of money.
    b. Maria wanted to start her own business and made a lot of money.
    c. Maria wanted to start her own business and had made a lot of money.

_____

12. a. He did not want to go to the party with us, so I did not ask him again if he is needing a ride.
    b. He did not want to go to the party with us, so I did not ask him again if he needs a ride.
    c. He did not want to go to the party with us, so I did not ask him again if he needed a ride.

_____

13. a. Last semester Saul took so many classes that he did not have enough time to study for any of them.
    b. Last semester Saul took so many classes that he was not having enough time to study for any of them.
    c. Last semester Saul took so many classes that he did not had enough time to study for any of them.

    _____

14. a. We had just gone to bed when we had heard a scream.
    b. We had just gone to bed when we heard a scream.
    c. We had just gone to bed when we hear a scream.

    _____

15. a. They see a storm approaching as they came over the top of the hill.
    b. They saw a storm approaching as they come over the top of the hill.
    c. They could see a storm approaching as they came over the top of the hill.

    _____

EXERCISE 40: EDITING FOR CLARITY – KEEPING VERB TENSES CONSISTENT

CORRESPONDS TO SECTION 41C IN *THE NEW MCGRAW-HILL HANDBOOK* AND SECTION 41B IN *A WRITER'S RESOURCE*

Instructions: Are the underlined verbs in the following items correct? If not, write the correct form of the verb in the space to the right. If the verb is correct, write *C* in the space.

EXAMPLE

Last year, drivers who used Route 28 <u>are</u> often delayed by construction.   *were*

---

1. In 1968, after the death of Dr. Martin Luther King, Jr., the Reverend Ralph Abernathy <u>become</u> head of the Southern Christian Leadership Conference.

   _____

2. When Charles Kingsley, an English clergyman, made disparaging remarks about Roman Catholic clergy, John Cardinal Newman <u>responds</u> with his *Apology*.

   _____

3. The Kiowa Indians, who now number about 10,000, <u>are</u> allied with the Comanches against further white settlement during the nineteenth century.

   _____

4. *Delicatessen* comes from two German words that <u>meant</u> "delicate" and "to eat."

   _____

5. Traveling through Africa last year, she <u>visits</u> parts of what was once Togoland.

   _____

6. My brother is a regular Mozart. He <u>is showing</u> interest in the violin ever since he was four years old.

   _____

7. The city of Philadelphia takes its name from an ancient Greek phrase that <u>meant</u> "brother love."

   _____

8. The Greeks believed that before Zeus came to power the universe <u>was</u> ruled by the Titans.

   _____

9. The sonnet, a fourteen-line poem popularized by Petrarch and Shakespeare, <u>was</u> also used by poets practicing their craft today.

    _____

10. When they looked through the telescope, they saw Jupiter's moon Ganymede, which the astronomer said <u>was</u> the biggest in our solar system.

    _____

11. The United Nations Educational, Scientific, and Cultural Organization (UNESCO), which makes its headquarters in Paris, <u>had been</u> in that city since its inception in 1946.

    _____

12. Before it joined the United States in 1845, Texas <u>was</u> an independent republic and before that, part of Mexico.

    _____

13. U.S. citizens began to settle in the Mexican territory of Texas when Stephen Austin <u>leads</u> a group of his countrymen there in 1821.

    _____

14. Luckily, Elena had gotten inoculated just before stepping on a rusty nail last summer; otherwise, she <u>would contract</u> tetanus.

    _____

15. Before the invention in 1731 of the sextant, an instrument used to take the height of stars above the horizon, sea navigation <u>was</u> more difficult.

    _____

EXERCISE 41: EDITING FOR CLARITY – FAULTY PARALLELISM

CORRESPONDS TO SECTION 42B IN *THE NEW MCGRAW-HILL HANDBOOK* AND SECTION 42A IN *A WRITER'S RESOURCE*

USING CATALYST	www.mhhe.com/nmhh www.mhhe.com/awr
For information and exercises on parallelism, go to Editing > Parallelism	

Instructions: The following items contain three versions of the same sentence. In the space provided, write the letter of the version that uses correct parallel structure.

EXAMPLE

a. Running a restaurant demands patience, it takes knowledge, and it also takes luck.
b. Running a restaurant demands patience, takes knowledge, and requiring luck.
c. Running a restaurant demands patience, knowledge, and luck.

c

---

1. a. New York City is famous for its Broadway plays, its Italian restaurants, and it has first-class stores.
   b. New York City is famous for its Broadway plays, Italian restaurants, and first-class stores.
   c. New York City is famous for Broadway plays, having Italian restaurants, and shopping in first-class stores.

   _____

2. a. Landing a man on the moon in 1969 took technical know-how, courage, and it required a lot of teamwork.
   b. Landing a man on the moon in 1969 took technical know-how, courage, and teamwork.
   c. Landing a man on the moon in 1969 took technical know-how, it took courage, and it required a lot of teamwork.

   _____

3. a. Before leaving for the weekend, we have to wash the dishes, make the beds, clean the house, and lock all the doors.
   b. Before leaving for the weekend, we have to wash the dishes, make the beds, cleaning the house, and locking all the doors.
   c. Before leaving for the weekend, we have to wash the dishes, and also make the beds, and make sure the house is clean, and check to see that all the doors are locked.

   _____

4. a. The scientific method is the systematic process of correctly forming and then to prove hypotheses.
   b. The scientific method is the systematic process of correctly forming and proving hypotheses.
   c. The scientific method is the systematic process of correctly forming hypotheses and then you prove them.

   _____

5. a. Although cars traditionally run on gasoline, more and more automakers are designing cars that run on diesel, ethanol, or powered by electricity.
   b. Although cars traditionally run on gasoline, more and more automakers are designing cars that run on diesel, on ethanol, or powered by electricity.
   c. Although cars traditionally run on gasoline, more and more automakers are designing cars that run on diesel, ethanol, or electricity.

   _____

6. a. Succeeding in school takes hard work, you need to be focused, and it requires dedication.
   b. Succeeding in school takes hard work, focus, and dedication.
   c. Succeeding in school requires hard work, it takes focus, and dedication.

   _____

7. a. Education has long been a focus in Scotland, which is famous for its many great universities, and also many famous thinkers have come from Scotland.
   b. Education has long been a focus in Scotland, which is famous for its many great universities and many famous thinkers.
   c. Education has long been a focus in Scotland, which is famous for its many great universities; also many famous thinkers have come from Scotland

   _____

8. a. Alfred Adler, the noted psychiatrist, argued that people are driven by feelings of inferiority and attempt to compensate by striving for competence, mastery, and to gain power.
   b. Alfred Adler, the noted psychiatrist, argued that people are driven by feelings of inferiority and attempt to compensate by striving for competence, mastery, and power.
   c. Alfred Adler, the noted psychiatrist, argued that people are driven by feelings of inferiority and attempting to compensate by striving for competence, mastery, and power.

   _____

9. a. As relief workers distributed high-energy foods to hungry children, helped dig latrines for emergency shelters, and while they were boiling water for safe drinking, they could hear the enemy's planes approaching.
   b. As relief workers distributed high-energy foods to hungry children, helped dig latrines for emergency shelters, and boiled water for safe drinking, they could hear the enemy's planes approaching.

c. As relief workers were distributing high-energy foods to hungry children and were helping to dig latrines for emergency shelters, they could hear the enemy's planes approaching even while they boiled water for safe drinking.

_____

10. a. In Canada's Wapusk National Park, the terrain is too daunting, they have many dangerous bears, and the frigid temperatures keep tourists away.
    b. In Canada's Wapusk National Park, the terrain is too daunting, the bears are dangerous, and the temperatures too frigid to attract tourists.
    c. In Canada's Wapusk National Park, the daunting terrain, the dangerous bears, and the frigid temperatures keep tourists away.

_____

EXERCISE 42: EDITING FOR CLARITY – MODIFIER PLACEMENT AND AMBIGUOUS MODIFIERS

CORRESPONDS TO SECTIONS 43B AND 43C IN *THE NEW MCGRAW-HILL HANDBOOK* AND SECTIONS 43A AND 43B IN *A WRITER'S RESOURCE*

USING CATALYST	www.mhhe.com/nmhh www.mhhe.com/awr
For information and exercises on misplaced modifiers, go to Editing > Misplaced Modifiers	

Instructions: The following items contain two versions of the same sentence. Write the letter of the correct version on the line to the right.

EXAMPLE

   a. Belinda rode a camel through the desert.
   b. Belinda rode through the desert a camel.

                                        a

---

1. a. He sat nervously on the edge of his seat as the movie got more and more exciting.
  b. He sat nervously as the movie got more and more exciting on the edge of his seat.

        _____

2. a. Jake read the sign written in Spanish on the side of the Mexican highway.
  b. Jake read the sign on the side of the Mexican highway written in Spanish.

        _____

3. a. May approached the stage carrying flowers.
  b. Carrying flowers, May approached the stage.

        _____

4. a. They climbed the high mountains wearing hiking boots.
  b. Wearing hiking boots, they climbed the high mountains.

        _____

5. a. Backed into a corner and beaten, the bell barely saved the fighter.
  b. Backed into a corner and beaten, the fighter was barely saved by the bell.

        _____

6. a. Blazing across the sky, the astronomer watched the comet.
   b. The astronomer watched the comet blazing across the sky.

   _____

7. a. While searching for a job, the classified advertising section of the newspaper was what I read.
   b. I read the classified advertising section of the newspaper while I was searching for a job.

   _____

8. a. Doing one amazing trick after another, the entire audience enjoyed the clever young magician.
   b. The entire audience enjoyed the clever young magician doing one amazing trick after another.

   _____

9. a. Needing a new coat of paint, Luis worked all afternoon in the bedroom.
   b. Luis worked all afternoon in the bedroom, which needed a new coat of paint.

   _____

10. a. Inaugurated in 2002, the Falkirk Wheel is vital to the rebirth of Britain's canals.
    b. Inaugurated in 2002, the rebirth of Britain's canals is dependent on the Falkirk Wheel.

    _____

EXERCISE 43: EDITING FOR CLARITY – FIXING DANGLING MODIFIERS

CORRESPONDS TO SECTION 43F IN *THE NEW MCGRAW-HILL HANDBOOK* AND SECTION 43E IN *A WRITER'S RESOURCE*

USING CATALYST	www.mhhe.com/nmhh www.mhhe.com/awr
For information and exercises on avoiding dangling modifiers, go to Editing > Dangling Modifiers	

Instructions: The following items contain three versions of the same sentence. Write the letter of the correct version on the line to the right.

EXAMPLE

a. Just before taking the test, my hands got sweaty.
b. Before I took the test, my hands got sweaty.
c. My hands got sweaty before taking the test.

b

---

1. a. Having played well offensively and defensively, the loss was bitter.
   b. Because the team played well offensively and defensively, the loss was bitter.
   c. The loss, having played well offensively and defensively, was bitter to the team.

   _____

2. a. Having cleaned the house, the garage was next.
   b. After cleaning the house, the garage was next.
   c. Having cleaned the house, they decided the garage was next.

   _____

3. a. While vacationing, my wallet was stolen.
   b. My wallet was stolen while on vacation.
   c. While I was on vacation, my wallet was stolen.

   _____

4. a. Holding your breath, your face will turn blue.
   b. If you hold your breath, your face will turn blue.
   c. Your face will turn blue holding your breath.

   _____

5. a. Suffering from exhaustion, Lindbergh's plane landed in Paris after crossing the Atlantic.

b. Suffering from exhaustion, Lindbergh landed his plane in Paris after crossing the Atlantic.

c. Suffering from exhaustion, after crossing the Atlantic, Lindbergh's plane landed in Paris.

_____

6. a. Marked by the development of advanced tools, during the Neolithic period humans evolved from hunters and gatherers to farmers living in fixed communities.

b. Marked by the development of advanced tools, humans evolved from hunters and gatherers to farmers living in fixed communities during the Neolithic period.

c. Marked by the development of advanced tools, the Neolithic period saw the evolution of humans from hunters and gatherers to farmers living in fixed communities.

_____

7. a. Shortly after making an alliance with the Soviets, the pact was broken.

b. Shortly after making an alliance with the Soviets, Hitler broke the pact.

c. The pact was broken shortly after making an alliance with the Soviets.

_____

8. a. Wearing one of the strangest hats I've ever seen, the car drove right through the center of town.

b. The car, wearing one of the strangest hats I've ever seen, drove right through the center of town.

c. Wearing one of the strangest hats I've ever seen, Aunt Jesse drove the car right through the center of town.

_____

9. a. Before taking the exam, the teacher was asked for pencils.

b. Pencils were requested of the teacher before taking the exam.

c. Before taking the exam, the students asked the teacher for pencils.

_____

10. a. They saw an elephant watching television at their friend's house.

b. Watching television, they saw an elephant at their friend's house.

c. Watching television at their friend's house, they saw an elephant.

_____

11. a. Waiting for the popcorn to finish cooking, they missed the beginning of the movie.

b. The movie began without them, waiting for the popcorn to finish cooking.

c. Waiting for the popcorn to finish cooking, the movie began without them.

_____

12. a. Lost in her purse, Lori couldn't find her keys.
    b. Lori couldn't find her keys, which were lost in her purse.
    c. Lori, lost in her purse, couldn't find her keys.

                                                             _____

13. a. After singing off-key for two hours and telling bad jokes between the songs, the audience grew tired.
    b. The audience grew tired of the performer, who sang off-key for two hours and told bad jokes between songs.
    c. Telling bad jokes and singing off-key for two hours, the audience grew tired.

                                                             _____

14. a. Unable to decide what classes to take, it was difficult to make a schedule.
    b. It was difficult to make a schedule, not knowing what classes to take.
    c. Unable to decide what classes to take, the student had difficulty making a schedule.

                                                             _____

15. a. The room got cold fast after we turned the heater off.
    b. The room got cold fast turning the heater off.
    c. Turning the heater off, the room got cold fast.

                                                             _____

EXERCISE 44: EDITING FOR CLARITY – COMBINING SHORT, CHOPPY SENTENCES

CORRESPONDS TO SECTION 44F IN *THE NEW MCGRAW-HILL HANDBOOK* AND SECTION 44D IN *A WRITER'S RESOURCE*

Instructions: Read the two sentences in each of the ten items below. Then choose the version that best combines the two. Write your answer in the space to the right.

EXAMPLE

The store was closing in five minutes.
Janice rushed to get her shopping done.   *c*

a. The store was closing in five minutes Janice rushed to get her shopping done.

b. The store was closing in five minutes, but Janice rushed to get her shopping done.

c. Janice rushed to get her shopping done because the store was closing in five minutes.

---

1. Atlantic City has miles of beautiful beaches.
   It also has many casinos.   _____

   a. Atlantic City has miles of beautiful beaches; also has many casinos.
   b. Atlantic City has miles of beautiful beaches, it also has many casinos.
   c. Atlantic City has miles of beautiful beaches; it also has many casinos.

2. Early motion pictures were often short and produced very quickly.
   Charlie Chaplin once made 34 films in 43 weeks.   _____

   a. Early motion pictures were often short and produced very quickly, but Charlie Chaplin once made 34 films in 43 weeks.
   b. Early motion pictures were often short and produced very quickly, Charlie Chaplin once made 34 films in 43 weeks.
   c. Early motion pictures were often short and produced very quickly; for example, Charlie Chaplin once made 34 films in 43 weeks.

3. Sigmund Freud believed dreams are windows to the unconscious.
   He argued that dreams represent unconscious wishes.   _____

   a. Believing dreams are windows to the unconscious; Sigmund Freud argued that dreams represent unconscious wishes.

b. Because Sigmund Freud believed dreams are windows to the unconscious, he argued that dreams represent unconscious wishes.

c. Sigmund Freud believed dreams are windows to the unconscious, he argued that dreams represent unconscious wishes.

4. The Industrial Revolution was a period of intense economic and social change.
It resulted from changes in manufacturing in the late eighteenth century. _____

a. Resulting from changes in manufacturing in the late eighteenth century; the Industrial Revolution was a period of intense economic and social change.

b. The Industrial Revolution was a period of intense economic and social change, it resulted from changes in manufacturing in the late eighteenth century.

c. Resulting from changes in manufacturing in the late eighteenth century, the Industrial Revolution was a period of intense economic and social change.

5. The tundra is a treeless area in arctic regions.
It supports many small shrubs and flowers. _____

a. The tundra is a treeless area in arctic regions, it supports many small shrubs and flowers.

b. The tundra is a treeless area in arctic regions, but it supports many small shrubs and flowers.

c. A treeless area in arctic regions; the tundra supports many small shrubs and flowers.

6. Franklin Roosevelt was handicapped.
He became president. _____

a. Franklin Roosevelt was handicapped, so he became president.

b. Although Franklin Roosevelt was handicapped, he became president.

c. Franklin Roosevelt was handicapped, he became president.

7. Many tenants in the building have pets.
The woman upstairs has three dogs, two cats, and a snake. _____

a. Many tenants in the building have pets; the woman upstairs has three dogs, two cats, and a snake.

b. Because many tenants in the building have pets, the woman upstairs has three dogs, two cats, and a snake.

c. Many tenants in the building have pets, but the woman upstairs has three dogs, two cats, and a snake.

8. While a college football star, Byron White won the Heisman Trophy.
President Kennedy later appointed White to the Supreme Court. _____

a. While a college football star, Byron White won the Heisman Trophy, President Kennedy later appointed White to the Supreme Court.
b. While a college football star, Byron White won the Heisman Trophy because President Kennedy later appointed White to the Supreme Court.
c. While a college football star, Byron White won the Heisman Trophy; President Kennedy later appointed White to the Supreme Court.

9. According to health experts, cigarette smoking is the leading cause of lung cancer. Many people continue to smoke cigarettes.

                                                   _____

a. According to health experts, cigarette smoking is the leading cause of lung cancer; however, many people continue to smoke cigarettes.
b. According to health experts, cigarette smoking is the leading cause of lung cancer, however, many people continue to smoke cigarettes.
c. According to health experts, cigarette smoking is the leading cause of lung cancer, so many people continue to smoke cigarettes.

10. Polar bears will dig temporary snow caves. These caves are called day dens. These dens provide shelter from nasty weather.

                                                 _____

a. Polar bears will dig temporary snow caves, called day dens, to provide shelter from nasty weather.
b. Polar bears will dig temporary snow caves, called day dens; to provide shelter from nasty weather
c. Polar bears will dig temporary dens, called day dens, and provide shelter from nasty weather.

EXERCISE 45: EDITING FOR CLARITY – ALTERNATIVES TO *BE* VERBS, AND ACTIVE VOICE

CORRESPONDS TO SECTIONS 46A AND 46B IN *THE NEW MCGRAW-HILL HANDBOOK* AND SECTIONS 46A AND 46B IN *A WRITER'S RESOURCE*

USING CATALYST	www.mhhe.com/nmhh www.mhhe.com/awr
For information and exercises on active verbs, go to Editing > Verbs and Verbals	

Instructions: One of the sentences in each set below is in the active voice; the other is in the passive voice. Identify the one that is in the active voice, and write the letter of that sentence in the space to the right.

EXAMPLE   a. Commuters take the train to their jobs in the city.
b. The train is taken by commuters to their jobs in the city.   *a*

---

1. a. Dr. Roberts is lecturing on Gothic architecture at 3:00 p.m.
    b. Gothic architecture is being lectured on by Dr. Roberts at 3:00 p.m.

    _____

2. a. Generally, a moderate position is maintained by King Abdullah of Jordan.
    b. Generally, King Abdullah of Jordan maintains a moderate position.

    _____

3. a. Someone just found evidence of a previously unknown Mesopotamian city.
    b. Evidence of a previously unknown Mesopotamian city has just been found.

    _____

4. a. Aware of the need to revive the economy of post-war Europe, the plan that now bears his name was devised by General George Marshall.
    b. Aware of the need to revive the economy of post-war Europe, General George Marshall devised the plan that now bears his name.

    _____

5. a. Modern Azerbaijan includes parts of the old kingdom of Armenia.
    b. Parts of the old kingdom of Armenia are included in modern Azerbaijan.

    _____

6. a. Following a low-fat diet can help people avoid arteriosclerosis, or hardening of the arteries.
   b. Arteriosclerosis, or hardening of the arteries, can be avoided if a low-fat diet is followed.

   _____

7. a. Centuries ago, many of the pharaohs' tombs had been opened and robbed.
   b. Centuries ago, robbers opened and robbed many of the pharaohs' tombs.

   _____

8. a. Someone had unlocked the door to Dr. Jekyll's laboratory.
   b. The door to Dr. Jekyll's laboratory had been unlocked.

   _____

9. a. The Chicago Institute of Art displays many priceless works, including an impressive Asian collection.
   b. Many priceless works, including an impressive Asian collection, are displayed at the Chicago Institute of Art.

   _____

10. a. In 1988, George H. W. Bush was elected president of the United States.
    b. In 1988, the people of the United States elected George H. W. Bush president.

   _____

EXERCISE 46: EDITING FOR CLARITY – THE ACTIVE VOICE

CORRESPONDS TO SECTIONS 46A AND 46B IN *THE NEW MCGRAW-HILL HANDBOOK* AND SECTIONS 46A AND 46B IN *A WRITER'S RESOURCE*

USING CATALYST	www.mhhe.com/nmhh www.mhhe.com/awr
For information and exercises on active verbs, go to Editing > Verbs and Verbals	

Instructions: Rewrite the sentences below in the active voice.

1. The ball was hit by John.

   _____

2. The home run was hit by Sandy.

   _____

3. Joanne was elected class president.

   _____

4. I was surprised by the quality of your essays.

   _____

5. Twenty-three enemy soldiers were taken prisoner.

   _____

6. The laboratory rats were set free by the animal rights activist.

   _____

7. The books, which had been checked out in large numbers by the students, were banned by the parent council and taken from the library shelves.

   _____

   _____

   _____

8. The dinner was prepared by a master chef and served by a team of waiters.

_____

_____

9. The report was mistakenly filed under the name Harry S Truman instead of Truman, Harry.

_____

_____

10. Enron's fraudulent accounting was blamed on several key executives of both Enron and Arthur Andersen.

_____

_____

EXERCISE 47: EDITING FOR CLARITY – BIASED OR SEXIST LANGUAGE

CORRESPONDS TO SECTION 48E IN *THE NEW MCGRAW-HILL HANDBOOK* AND SECTION 47E IN *A WRITER'S RESOURCE*

USING CATALYST	www.mhhe.com/nmhh www.mhhe.com/awr
For information and exercises on appropriate language, go to Editing > Word Choice	

Instructions: Revise the following items in the spaces provided to remove sexist pronouns.

EXAMPLE   If a person wants to stay healthy, he should avoid junk food.

People who want to stay healthy should avoid junk food.

---

1. If someone needs a loan, he should never borrow from my Uncle Shifty.

   _____

2. Some countries require a visitor to bring his visa.

   _____

3. The French chef is famous for his culinary skills all over the world.

   _____

4. Every senator was expected to vote his conscience, but few did.

   _____

5. A nurse should pay attention to changes in her patients' appetites.

   _____

6. A firefighter must keep himself in good physical condition.

   _____

7. In communist Rumania, a farmer ran the risk of having his land appropriated by the government without appeal.

_____

8. Each infantry soldier must wear a heavy pack on his back.

_____

9. A student enrolled in Photography I must develop his own film.

_____

10. Anyone who has pride in himself would never dress as Otto does.

_____

EXERCISE 48: EDITING FOR CLARITY – APPROPRIATE LANGUAGE

CORRESPONDS TO SECTION 48 IN *THE NEW MCGRAW-HILL HANDBOOK* AND SECTION 47 IN *A WRITER'S RESOURCE*

USING CATALYST	www.mhhe.com/nmhh www.mhhe.com/awr
For information and exercises on appropriate language, go to Editing > Word Choice	

Instructions: Revise the following sentences in the spaces provided to eliminate slang, jargon, colloquialisms, and problems with idioms. If you have problems identifying such phrases, you may want to ask your teacher to explain why these phrases are problematic.

EXAMPLE   They got their kicks from blasting the car radio.

They enjoyed playing the car radio extremely loudly.

---

1. When the Americans split from Saigon, the North Vietnamese, against whom the US troups had fought until 1973, took over.

   _____

   _____

2. The bottom line was that the American government knew the war in Vietnam was a loser.

   _____

   _____

3. In 1954, Vietnam had been cut up into the North and the South on account of the Geneva Convention, which ended the French Indochina War.

   _____

   _____

4. That conflict dragged on from 1946 to 1954, and the French simply got sick and tired of sacrificing so many men and so much treasure in a losing battle.

   _____

   _____

5. As soon as the French bolted, Commie guerrillas from the North came down the road and attacked the South.

_____

_____

6. Then the United States gave it a go, at first trying out a force of military advisory personnel in support of the South Vietnamese government.

_____

_____

7. The Communists were getting plenty of goodies from their Russian allies, and their troops had primo training compared with that of the South Vietnamese soldiers, so the Americans figured they had better send in real troops, not just advisors.

_____

_____

_____

8. The Tonkin Gulf Resolution of 1964 committed even more American military assets to the theater of operations, and the United States soon had forces at optimum levels for major operations. Indeed, this was a field of battle very different from any other the United States had ever engaged in.

_____

_____

_____

_____

9. When the North launched the Tet Offensive in 1968, the Americans and the South Vietnamese had a hard time getting it together and at first got pretty beat up, so American public opinion went sour on the war.

_____

_____

_____

10. A cease-fire was signed when the opposing sides interfaced in Paris in 1974; however, the situation was not finalized until the North gave the South the old heave-ho in 1975, renaming Saigon, the South's former capital, Ho Chi Min City.

_____

_____

_____

_____

EXERCISE 49: EDITING FOR CLARITY – EXACT LANGUAGE AND GLOSSARY OF USAGE

CORRESPONDS TO SECTIONS 49 AND 50 IN *THE NEW MCGRAW-HILL HANDBOOK* AND SECTIONS 48 AND 50 IN *A WRITER'S RESOURCE*

USING CATALYST	www.mhhe.com/nmhh www.mhhe.com/awr
For information and exercises on exact language, go to Editing > Word Choice	

Instructions: Revise the following sentences in the spaces provided to eliminate incorrect word choice. Some sentences may contain more than one error.

EXAMPLE   We never should of entered the marathon.

We never should have entered the marathon.

---

1. During World War II, Hitler had many Germans convinced that they could not loose.

   _____

   _____

2. Now that the Soviet Union is no more, the principle reason for the Cold War has disappeared.

   _____

   _____

3. Most South Africans have excepted, indeed rejoiced over, the demise of apartheid.

   _____

   _____

4. The dock was not stationery; it could be moved from one part of the bay to the other.

   _____

   _____

5. The site of India's Taj Mahal takes your breathe away.

_____

6. The camel was brought to the desserts of North Africa from Asia because of its ability to go without water for long periods.

_____

_____

7. Your lucky that you were in a large car; otherwise you would have sustained more severe injuries in the wreck.

_____

_____

8. The danger is to great to be taken litely.

_____

9. In the seventeenth century, the Dutch imported Muslim slaves from Indonesia to there colony in southern Africa; to this day, alot of the descendants of those slaves practice Islam.

_____

_____

_____

10. It is all together foolhardy to travel to the rain forest without taking precautions against malaria and other diseases one might contact there.

_____

_____

EXERCISE 50: EDITING FOR CLARITY – CLICHÉS

CORRESPONDS TO SECTION 49F IN *THE NEW MCGRAW-HILL HANDBOOK* AND SECTION 48D IN *A WRITER'S RESOURCE*

Instructions: Revise the following sentences in the spaces provided to eliminate clichés.

> **EXAMPLE**   Mary's recommendations were as good as gold.
>
> *Mary's recommendations were reliable.*

1. The issue of reforming Social Security has always been a political hot potato.

    _____

2. President Eisenhower was not long-winded; when speaking, he was always short and sweet.

    _____

    _____

3. H. M. Warner was as cool as a cucumber when, in 1927, he claimed that no one wanted "to hear actors talk."

    _____

    _____

4. Because of increased competition, deregulation, and rising fuel costs, many airlines went under in the 1980s.

    _____

    _____

5. In 1945, the Germans and the Japanese knew that they had to face the cold, hard fact that their countries would be occupied by the Allies.

    _____

    _____

6. People should avoid clichés like the plague; in fact, they should try to be original at all costs.

_____

_____

7. The President was asked if his better half would be involved in drafting a new budget that would force the government to tighten its belt.

_____

_____

8. Certain government entitlement programs are considered sacred cows, but they may bite the dust if Congress has its way.

_____

_____

9. The young engineer, who was green with envy over the success her sister had achieved as a stockbroker, decided to climb the ladder of success by putting her nose to the grindstone.

_____

_____

10. With his eyes glued to the television set, Albert sat on the edge of his seat and watched a rerun of Hitchcock's film classic *Psycho,* but during the famous shower scene, he turned white as a ghost.

_____

_____

EDITING EXERCISE 8: EDITING FOR CLARITY – SENTENCE STRUCTURE ERRORS (CONFUSING SHIFTS, FAULTY PARALLELISM, MISPLACED AND DANGLING MODIFIERS)

CORRESPONDS TO SECTIONS 41–43 IN *THE NEW MCGRAW-HILL HANDBOOK* AND SECTIONS 41–43 IN *A WRITER'S RESOURCE*

Instructions: Rewrite the following paragraphs in the spaces provided to eliminate verb tense and voice shifts, to correct problems with parallelism, and to eliminate dangling or misplaced modifiers.

Archimedes of Syracuse

Born in 287 BC, the Greek city of Syracuse, which is located in southeastern Sicily, was the home of Archimedes. He was a scientist, mathematician, inventor, and a man who helped develop modern engineering methods. Among his most important contributions are those in geometry and physics. Finding a way to measure the volume of a sphere, principles were discovered that relate to modern calculus, a mathematical study that developed nearly two thousand years after his death. Archimedes's principle, his most famous discovery, is still used to calculate the weight of a body immersed in a liquid. Legend has it that he came upon this principle while taking a bath. So excited was he by his discovery that he sat up, jumped out of the tub, and he ran around shouting "Eureka!"--ancient Greek for "I have found it"-- neglecting to put on his clothes. One of his most famous inventions is Archimedes's screw, which is still in use today in some countries as a way for drawing water. Archimedes died during the Roman invasion of his city in 212 BC. While trying to solve a knotty mathematical problem, a Roman soldier accosted him. The soldier got angry when the scientist refused to go with him until he had finished solving the problem and was killed.

_____

_____

_____

_____

_____

_____

_____

_____

Athens and the Golden Age

The capital of Greece, Athens is a modern city dating from about 1337 AD. However, ancient Athens, situated on the site upon which the present city is located, was founded in the seventh century BC. It was destroyed by the Persians under Xerxes in 480 BC, but Pericles rebuilds it and makes it an even more important city. The Greek ruler who ushered in the Golden Age, Pericles supports the rise of philosophy, literature, and he is most famous for his love of the arts. During this time, the city was a commercial and artistic center, and it was also a formidable political power. The leader of a group of independent Greek city-states, civilization's first attempt at democracy was made in Athens. Today, through the plays of Sophocles, Aeschylus, Euripides, and Aristophanes, Athenians can also boast that their city gave birth to Western drama. They can also claim Athens as the birthplace of Western philosophy because of the teachings of Socrates, Plato, and a man called Aristotle.

_____

_____

_____

_____

_____

_____

_____

_____

Jainism

A unique philosophy and religion, India in the sixth century BC saw the rise of Jainism. Today, about four million Jains live in various parts of the country. Translated as "spiritual conqueror," the religion takes its name from the word *jina,* which was also the name of one of its ancient prophets and founders. Jainism begins as a reaction to the practice of animal sacrifice in an early Hindu cult. Thus, one of the central doctrines of the faith is that no living animal should be harmed. Jains are strict vegetarians, and not even the smallest insect is destroyed by them. Indeed, they maintain shelters where sick, dying, or animals that have been injured are cared for. Jains believe only that by living a life of asceticism and denial can one reach perfection. Through such behavior, they teach, one is able to liberate the soul from the endless cycle of rebirth and perfection beyond the material world can be reached.

_____

_____

EDITING EXERCISE 9: EDITING FOR CLARITY – BIASED AND SEXIST LANGUAGE

CORRESPONDS TO SECTION 48E IN *THE NEW MCGRAW-HILL HANDBOOK* AND SECTION 47E IN *A WRITER'S RESOURCE*

Instructions: Rewrite the following paragraph in the spaces provided to eliminate problems with sexist language.

Gateway to the New World

Ellis Island was opened in 1892 to process the ever-growing stream of immigrants fleeing Europe. At its height in the years before World War I, Ellis Island became the gateway to America for the European immigrant. Almost without exception, if he had crossed the Atlantic, he would have to pass through the Ellis Island's immigration center before beginning his life in a new world. For nearly twenty years around the turn of the century, more than a million immigrants per year were processed through Ellis Island. In fact, historians estimate that forty percent of all Americans can trace their families back to an ancestor who arrived on this small island in New York harbor in the shadow of the Statue of Liberty. Typically, he would have arrived with his family, but, in many cases, he arrived alone, working here for several years and then calling for the rest of the family after he had saved enough money for their passage. The first Americans the immigrant met were, in most cases, immigration officers, who, dressed like policemen, often seemed intimidating to the newcomer. These men checked his papers to make sure that he had no criminal record and that his emigration from his home country had been legitimate. Finally, he was examined by a member of the health service. Such a man held tremendous power, for if he found that the newcomer suffered from even the slightest ailment, he could order that he be quarantined for an indefinite period or, worse, that he be shipped back. After 1924 the flood of immigrants decreased, and the facilities at Ellis Island were closed and abandoned in 1954. Recently, however, Ellis Island was renovated and turned into a national park. Today, a ferry takes the sons and grandsons of immigrants across the harbor to visit the splendid exhibits that reveal the terrible life that millions of immigrants had to endure in order to become Americans. Indeed, anyone who visits can stroll along a massive stone wall that lists millions of immigrant names and, most likely, find one that matches his own. Thus, Ellis Island again welcomes floods of people arriving by boat each year. It is one of the most visited parks in the nation.

_____

_____

_____

_____

_____

EDITING EXERCISE 10: EDITING FOR CLARITY – APPROPRIATE LANGUAGE

CORRESPONDS TO SECTION 48 IN *THE NEW MCGRAW-HILL HANDBOOK* AND SECTION 47 IN *A WRITER'S RESOURCE*

Instructions: Rewrite the following paragraph in the spaces provided to eliminate problems with tone and diction. In the process, make sure to include necessary words that have been intentionally left out and to eliminate clichés.

Table Manners

The kinds table manners we normally use in an expensive restaurant, at a diner, or even at home are hardly like those people used to use in the past. In fact, those we might see were we able to travel back in time and attend a meal served in the Middle Ages are very different from today. In the olden days, people did not use a spoon to eat their soup; they simply chugged it down directly from a large bowl. Meats and vegetables weren't served daintily with each person getting his or her own portion. Instead, people dug with their hands and scooped portions of grub from a common bowl that got passed one person to another. If you were hungrier then the next guy, you had to stick your hand first. Forks did not come on to the scene until the sixteenth century. The knowledge that disease-causing germs could be spread from one person to the other wasn't fully excepted until the nineteenth century. Thus, it is safe to say that medieval dinners didn't no beans about bacteriology and the communicability of diseases. So no one made a big deal of washing before chowing down. Drinking cups for each diner were as rare as hens' teeth, and people often drank from a common vessel, passing it during the coarse of the meal. When people finished up, it stands to reason that they did not wipe their mouths with napkins; instead, they used their sleeves or the tablecloth, and some (this might sound really gross) even blew their noses into a common cloth.

_____

_____

_____

_____

_____

_____

_____

Linen

A vegetable fiber derived from flax plant has given us linen, perhaps the oldest known textile. Its use goes way back, at least to the Stone Age. Archeologists have found whole bunches of linen cloth in digs of Neolithic sites where the Lake Dwellers of Switzerland once hung out. In the Nile Valley of Egypt evidence of linen weaving dates back more than six thousand years; the bodies of the Egyptian kings were wrapped in linen cloth (it's a crying shame that we still don't know all the secrets of Egyptian mummification). A sure-fire way to produce good flax is to grow it in swampy, mild lowlands. In recent times, France, Holland, and Germany have done an outstanding job of producing high-quality linen. Over the past century other fabrics have come to the fore and have replaced linen as the fabric of choice; however, make no mistake--until well into the eighteenth century, linen was still king in the world of textiles.

_____

_____

_____

_____

_____

_____

_____

_____

EDITING EXERCISE 11: EDITING FOR CLARITY – WORDY SENTENCES

CORRESPONDS TO SECTION 38 IN *THE NEW MCGRAW-HILL HANDBOOK* AND SECTION 38 IN *A WRITER'S RESOURCE*

Instructions: Rewrite the following paragraph in the spaces provided to eliminate repetition and make it more direct.

Tail of the Comet

The word *comet* originally derived from an ancient Greek word that means "long-haired" in that language. Comets are relatively small bodies of material that travel around the sun in solar orbits which have been described as elliptical paths. As comets reach nearer and nearer to the sun and get within close proximity of this heavenly body, light causes the melting of icy type matter at the nucleus of the comet's center, leaving behind in its wake gases and bits of dust particles that have come together to form the comet's tail, the very thing which gave the comet its ancient name in the first place. While often appearing as only a fuzzy light in the nighttime sky, comets can be very, very long, measuring millions and millions of miles in length, all the way from nose to tail. In actuality, there are really two types of comets: short-period comets, which go through their complete orbits in less than two-hundred-year periods, and long-term comets, which pass the sun at time intervals of thousands or even millions of years.

_____

_____

_____

_____

_____

_____

_____

_____

_____

EXERCISE 51: EDITING FOR CORRECTNESS – COMMAS

CORRESPONDS TO SECTION 51 IN *THE NEW MCGRAW-HILL HANDBOOK* AND SECTION 57 IN *A WRITER'S RESOURCE*

USING CATALYST	**www.mhhe.com/nmhh** **www.mhhe.com/awr**
For information and exercises on commas, go to **Editing > Commas**	

Instructions: Some sentences below are missing commas. If the sentence needs a comma or commas, write them in. If the sentence is correct, write *C* after it.

EXAMPLE

When Susan cooked her husband usually grimaced.

When Susan cooked, her husband usually grimaced.

---

1. No matter how hard he banged the door would not open.

2. While Marie painted her friends did the laundry.

3. To Helen eating is the best exercise.

4. As Matt cooked Anna stirred the soup.

5. Surprised by his wife Roger fell off the chair.

6. After Billy ate the cat began to purr.

7. The show opened on Monday not Sunday.

8. "The Greeks do not fight like heroes," said Winston Churchill "the heroes fight like Greeks."

9. Every time I go to the beach it rains.

10. While the thieves escaped the police were following a false lead.

EXERCISE 52: EDITING FOR CORRECTNESS – COMMA USE—
INTRODUCTORY WORD GROUPS

CORRESPONDS TO SECTION 51D IN *THE NEW MCGRAW-HILL HANDBOOK* AND SECTION 57A IN *A WRITER'S RESOURCE*

Using Catalyst	www.mhhe.com/nmhh www.mhhe.com/awr
For information and exercises on commas, go to Editing > Commas	

Instructions: A comma is needed in each of the items below to set off an introductory element from the rest of the sentence. Decide where the comma belongs, and write it in.

> **EXAMPLE**   As I was walking up the street it began to rain.
>
> *As I was walking up the street, it began to rain.*

1. As I was preparing to return to the United States I found that I had misplaced my passport.

2. In fact I couldn't find my wallet either.

3. Fortunately I wasn't in a hurry.

4. When I talked to the security officer he told me he would take personal care of my case.

5. However it took seven hours to straighten out the passport problem.

6. Second only to that of China India's population is now approaching one billion.

7. Created by the collision of a huge island into the Asian mainland more than fifty million years ago the Himalayas soar skyward over the northern frontiers of the Indian subcontinent.

8. When India won its independence from Britain in 1947 it was immediately partitioned into Hindu India and Muslim Pakistan, which consisted of two widely separated areas known as West Pakistan and East Pakistan (Bengal).

9. Because the Bengalis of East Pakistan believed that they were being denied political and economic advantages enjoyed by West Pakistanis they declared their independence in 1971 and established the independent nation of Bangladesh.

10. Having also been under British rule for several decades Burma, which is east of Bangladesh, received its independence in 1948.

EXERCISE 53: EDITING FOR CORRECTNESS – COMMA USE—ITEMS IN A SERIES

CORRESPONDS TO SECTION 51B IN *THE NEW MCGRAW-HILL HANDBOOK* AND SECTION 57B IN *A WRITER'S RESOURCE*

USING CATALYST	**www.mhhe.com/nmhh** **www.mhhe.com/awr**
For information and exercises on commas, go to Editing > Commas	

Instructions: One or more commas are needed in the sentences below. Decide where the comma or commas belong, and write them in.

EXAMPLE

Berlin Bucharest Budapest and Bern are some of the capital cities of Europe that begin with the letter *B*.

Berlin, Bucharest, Budapest, and Bern are some of the capital cities of Europe that begin with the letter B.

---

1. The Delaware River starts in upstate New York crosses the Appalachian Mountains at the Water Gap flows between New Jersey and Pennsylvania and reaches the Atlantic Ocean near Delaware.

2. George Washington crossed the Delaware River on a cold windy and snowy night in January.

3. Saying "I have nothing to offer but blood toil tears and sweat," Winston Churchill accepted the office of prime minister of England at the start of World War II.

4. By 1940, Britain was at war in Europe Asia and Africa.

5. After the war, Churchill devoted himself to writing painting travel and politics.

6. The Black Death was a plague that devastated Europe in the fourteenth century. It originated in China Mongolia and other parts of Asia.

7. It made its way west when an army from Asia catapulted corpses of plague victims into the Crimean city it was besieging in 1347. From there it moved to North Africa to Southern Italy and eventually to all other parts of Europe.

8. The first instance of the plague raged for three years, from 1347 to 1350. However, it reappeared in 1361-63 1369-71 1374-75 1390 and 1400.

9. The disease struck down poor and rich alike, both peasant and noble. It was responsible for the death of Queen Eleanor of Aragon King Alfonso XI of Castile the daughter of King Edward III of England and two Canterbury archbishops.

10. More than a third of Europe's population died because of the plague. As a result, Europe experienced a shortage of skilled and peasant labor a reduction in the amount of land that could be cultivated and an increase in wages for artisans and peasants alike.

EXERCISE 54: EDITING FOR CORRECTNESS – COMMA USE—INDEPENDENT CLAUSES JOINED BY A COORDINATING CONJUNCTION

CORRESPONDS TO SECTION 51A IN *THE NEW MCGRAW-HILL HANDBOOK* AND SECTION 57C IN *A WRITER'S RESOURCE*

Using Catalyst	www.mhhe.com/nmhh www.mhhe.com/awr
For information and exercises on commas, go to Editing > Commas	

Instructions: A comma is needed in each of the sentences below. Decide where the comma belongs, and write it in.

EXAMPLE   I burned the steak but Fred ate it anyway.

I burned the steak, but Fred ate it anyway.

---

1. Thomas Jefferson was opposed to the formation of political parties but he is credited as one of the founders of the party system in American politics.

2. Lech Walesa led the Solidarity labor movement in Poland and he became the first freely elected president of that nation.

3. Catherine the Great was born in Germany in 1729 yet she became one of Russia's greatest leaders.

4. Pegasus is the name given to the mythical winged horse and it is also the name of a constellation in the northern sky.

5. Summers in Sicily can get quite hot for this island off the coast of Italy is close to the equator.

6. The young wild dogs yelped loudly yet they posed no danger to the onlookers.

7. The Ndoki River is home to leopards, gorillas, elephants, and chimpanzees, some of which have never encountered human beings for the river is deep within the jungles of central Africa.

8. Many people are afraid of spiders but the Piaroa peoples of Venezuela cook and eat spiders the size of large dinner plates during holiday celebrations.

9. Elk, which are docile if left alone, will attack human beings who provoke them so remember to keep your distance when you come upon these magnificent animals.

10. She will eat one of the ostrich burgers we have prepared or she will have to settle for some alligator fricassee.

EXERCISE 55: EDITING FOR CORRECTNESS – COMMA USE—COORDINATE ADJECTIVES

CORRESPONDS TO SECTION 51C IN *THE NEW MCGRAW-HILL HANDBOOK* AND SECTION 57D IN *A WRITER'S RESOURCE*

USING CATALYST	www.mhhe.com/nmhh www.mhhe.com/awr
For information and exercises on commas, go to Editing > Commas	

Instructions: Some sentences below are missing commas. If the sentence needs a comma or commas, write them in. If the sentence is correct as is, write *C* after it.

EXAMPLE   The steep winding road led up the hill to the Acropolis.

The steep, winding road led up the hill to the Acropolis.

---

1. The timber rattlesnake is a poisonous yellowish-brown reptile that lives in the United States.

2. My teacher told me to speak in a clear loud voice for my oral presentation.

3. Last week I bought a long heavy coat for winter.

4. The dry mountainous terrain of southern Greece is not well suited for farming.

5. Old gnarled olive trees dot the hillsides.

6. Zulu is a beautiful rhythmic language spoken by some native peoples of South Africa.

7. Mercury is the only common metal that exists as a liquid at ordinary temperatures.

8. Modern biomedical research practices are often the subject of intense ethical scrutiny.

9. Dwali, the Hindu Festival of Lights, commemorates the return to northern India of Lord Ram and Sita after they defeated the fierce demonic king of Sri Lanka.

10. A recent eruption between two large volcanoes in Iceland has revealed much to geologists about the formation of the region's dramatic ice-capped landscape.

EXERCISE 56: EDITING FOR CORRECTNESS – COMMA USE—NONESSENTIAL ADDITIONS TO A SENTENCE

CORRESPONDS TO SECTION 51E IN *THE NEW MCGRAW-HILL HANDBOOK* AND SECTION 57E IN *A WRITER'S RESOURCE*

USING CATALYST	www.mhhe.com/nmhh www.mhhe.com/awr
For information and exercises on commas, go to Editing > Commas	

Instructions: Some sentences below are missing commas. If the sentence needs a comma or commas, write them in. If the sentence is correct, write *C* after it.

EXAMPLE   This book it seems was left out in the rain.

This book, it seems, was left out in the rain.

---

1. Indians who inhabited the plains of North America include the Pawnee, the Omaha, and the Blackfoot.

2. New York City which was originally called New Amsterdam was first settled by the Dutch.

3. The Taj Mahal which is in India was built by a Mogul emperor.

4. The first person who ate an artichoke was very brave.

5. Babe Ruth the famous Yankee baseball player began his career in Boston.

6. Students who don't study do poorly in this class.

7. Many animals that were once on the verge of extinction are making dramatic comebacks.

8. The passenger pigeon which was once very common has disappeared forever.

9. Some people who live in Sicily speak a dialect of ancient Greek.

10. Rhodes a beautiful Greek island was part of Italy until 1947.

EXERCISE 57: EDITING FOR CORRECTNESS – COMMA USE—PARTS OF DATES, LETTERS, ADDRESSES, TITLES, AND NUMBERS

CORRESPONDS TO SECTION 51I IN *THE NEW MCGRAW-HILL HANDBOOK* AND SECTION 57I IN *A WRITER'S RESOURCE*

USING CATALYST	www.mhhe.com/nmhh www.mhhe.com/awr
For information and exercises on commas, go to Editing > Commas	

Instructions: Decide where the commas are needed in the sentences below, and write them in. If a sentence is correct, write *C* after it.

EXAMPLE   World War I ended on November 11 1918.

World War I ended on November 11, 1918.

---

1. Martha was born in Denver Colorado.

2. We were married at the flower festival in Philadelphia on July 27 1996.

3. My first car lasted almost 300000 miles, but my last car died at 90000.

4. Winning 1000000 dollars in a lottery could cause as many problems as it solves.

5. After leaving the White House, President Eisenhower retired to a farm in Gettysburg Pennsylvania.

6. Selkirk is a town in southeastern Manitoba Canada.

7. The university decided to hire two new professors: Phil Osophie MA and Rosetta Stone PhD.

8. Dr. Martin Luther King Jr. was perhaps the best-known civil rights leader in the world.

9. Laura Litigious Esq and Daryl Dentum DDS were married on November 15 1997.

10. Nearly 5000 piled into the cathedral to hear an appeal by Fr. Joseph Andreas SJ, who had traveled thousands of miles to seek support for the mission he had established in a small village near Monterey Mexico.

EXERCISE 58: EDITING FOR CORRECTNESS – COMMON MISUSES OF THE COMMA

CORRESPONDS TO SECTIONS 51K–51Q IN *THE NEW MCGRAW-HILL HANDBOOK* AND SECTIONS 57K–57O IN *A WRITER'S RESOURCE*

Using Catalyst	www.mhhe.com/nmhh www.mhhe.com/awr
For information and exercises on commas, go to Editing > Commas	

Instructions: Some of the sentences below have unnecessary commas. Circle or underline any commas that are not needed. If a sentence is correct, write *C* after it.

EXAMPLE

A long, hard drought in the 1930s, created dust-bowl conditions in the Midwest.

1. Monrovia, is the capital of Liberia.

2. The Oder River, flows through Poland.

3. Thomas Jefferson was both a farmer, and an architect.

4. Thomas Jefferson, was also the author of the Declaration of Independence.

5. The house on Schalk's Crossing Road was, surrounded by fields and forests.

6. The deep, blue, water of the Aegean Sea has been the subject of poetry since the days of Homer.

7. Tuberculosis patients were often advised to move to the Southwest, because of the hot, dry climate there.

8. President Roosevelt looked thin, and tired at the Yalta Conference.

9. I enjoy reading, Edgar Allan Poe on dark, stormy nights.

10. Alex often, visits the neighbors.

EXERCISE 59: EDITING FOR CORRECTNESS – SEMICOLONS

CORRESPONDS TO SECTION 52 IN *THE NEW MCGRAW-HILL HANDBOOK* AND SECTION 58 IN *A WRITER'S RESOURCE*

USING CATALYST	www.mhhe.com/nmhh www.mhhe.com/awr
For information and exercises on semicolons, go to Editing > Semicolons	

Instructions: Some of the sentences below are missing semicolons. If the sentence needs a semicolon, write it in. If the sentence is correct, write *C* after it.

EXAMPLE

West Point was originally a fort on the Hudson River for almost two centuries it has served as a military college.

West Point was originally a fort on the Hudson <u>River; for</u> almost two centuries it has served as a military college.

---

1. Around the turn of the century Thomas Edison frequently went on camping trips with John Burroughs, the naturalist Henry Ford, the automobile manufacturer and Harvey Firestone, the rubber manufacturer.

2. The Titanic was designed to be unsinkable nevertheless, it sank on its maiden voyage.

3. Tiring of his creation, Sir Arthur Conan Doyle killed Sherlock Holmes in what should have been his final adventure later the writer brought Holmes back to life in other stories.

4. Richard and John Plantagenet were medieval English kings they were the sons of Henry II.

5. I've never been to Europe as a matter of fact, I've never been anywhere but here before.

6. Lonnie was two hours late for work this morning the bridge was closed because of an accident.

7. John Ciardi was famous for his poetry he also translated Dante's *Inferno*.

8. Hong Kong was once a British colony in 1997 it gained its independence.

9. Theodore Roosevelt ran for president as an independent in 1912 however, he lost the race to Woodrow Wilson.

10. Many people blamed President Hoover for the Great Depression, which began in 1929 as a result, he lost the next election to Franklin D. Roosevelt.

EXERCISE 60: EDITING FOR CORRECTNESS – COLONS

CORRESPONDS TO SECTION 53 IN *THE NEW MCGRAW-HILL HANDBOOK* AND SECTION 59 IN *A WRITER'S RESOURCE*

USING CATALYST	www.mhhe.com/nmhh www.mhhe.com/awr
For information and exercises on colons, go to Editing > Colons	

Instructions: Decide if the sentences below need colons. If they do, write them in. If a sentence is correct, write *C* after it.

EXAMPLE

France is famous for many culinary delights cheese, bread, and most of all, wine.

France is famous for many culinary <u>delights: cheese</u>, bread, and most of all, wine.

---

1. After dinner we ordered my favorite dessert apple pie.

2. Visitors to New York can look forward to many unique sights the Statue of Liberty, Ellis Island, Broadway, and Yankee Stadium.

3. The first plane arrives at 300 p.m.

4. The young doctor was the only person the villagers would trust she was their savior.

5. The mechanic stated his conclusion bluntly "I can't fix this car."

6. Three important rivers flow through Turkey the Euphrates, the Tigris, and the Irmak.

7. You need three qualities to succeed energy, courage, and perseverance.

8. As a young man, my grandfather had three passions family, work, and opera.

9. The detective confronted the suspects gathered together in the room "You all had ample opportunity to murder Sir Charles."

10. The rent on our new apartment covered all utilities including electricity, heat, and water.

EXERCISE 61: EDITING FOR CORRECTNESS – APOSTROPHES

CORRESPONDS TO SECTION 61 IN *THE NEW MCGRAW-HILL HANDBOOK* AND SECTION 60 IN *A WRITER'S RESOURCE*

USING CATALYST	www.mhhe.com/nmhh www.mhhe.com/awr
For information and exercises on apostrophes, go to Editing > Apostrophes	

Instructions: Some of the sentences below need apostrophes; others have unnecessary apostrophes. If an apostrophe is needed, write it in. Circle or underline any unnecessary apostrophes.

EXAMPLE

Washingtons birthday was originally celebrated on February 22.

Washington's birthday was originally celebrated on February 22.

1. Eugene O'Neill wrote *A Long Days Journey into Night*.

2. The highways twists and turns made the trip both exciting and dangerous.

3. Sohanna and Nadeems apartment is on the third floor.

4. I hope its not going to rain tomorrow.

5. The woodpecker lost it's house when the old tree fell in the storm.

6. Lisa got two As and two Bs this semester.

7. John Dillinger was number one on the FBIs most-wanted list at the time of his death.

8. UCLAs campus is one of the prettiest in the country.

9. Hitler planned to conquer all the nation's of Europe.

10. Under Hitler, Germany sought its' place in the sun.

EXERCISE 62: EDITING FOR CORRECTNESS – QUOTATION MARKS

CORRESPONDS TO SECTION 54 IN *THE NEW MCGRAW-HILL HANDBOOK* AND SECTION 61 IN *A WRITER'S RESOURCE*

USING CATALYST	www.mhhe.com/nmhh www.mhhe.com/awr
For information and exercises on quotation marks, go to Editing > Quotation Marks	

Instructions: Some of the sentences below are missing quotation marks. Write in the quotation marks where they belong.

EXAMPLE

Language shows a man, said Ben Johnson. Speak, that I may know you.

"Language shows a man," said Ben Johnson. "Speak, that I may know you."

---

1. Be careful about reading health books, said Mark Twain. You may die of a misprint.

2. My dentist was briefly mentioned in an article called License to Steal.

3. Show me a hero, said F. Scott Fitzgerald, and I'll write you a tragedy.

4. Every being, noted Simone Weil, cries out silently to be read differently.

5. Mack the Knife was recorded by Louis Armstrong, Bobby Darren, and many other great singers.

6. According to my professor, Bartleby the Scrivener by Herman Melville is the best short story ever written.

7. Headless Body Found in Topless Bar has to be one of the oddest headlines ever printed.

8. Bill said, I was surprised to hear Mary shout Fire!

9. Please all, and you will please none, said Aesop.

10. Edgar Allan Poe sold his poem The Raven for about ten dollars.

EXERCISE 63: EDITING FOR CORRECTNESS – PERIODS, QUESTION MARKS, AND EXCLAMATION POINTS

CORRESPONDS TO SECTION 56 IN *THE NEW MCGRAW-HILL HANDBOOK* AND SECTIONS 62A–62C IN *A WRITER'S RESOURCE*

USING CATALYST	www.mhhe.com/nmhh
	www.mhhe.com/awr
For information and exercises on end punctuation, go to Editing > End Punctuation	

Instructions: Choose the correct end punctuation for the sentences below. Write your answer in the space provided.

EXAMPLE

John Maynard Keynes, a British economist, advocated government intervention to lessen unemployment and control economic conditions

    a.   A period (.)
    b.   A question mark (?)
    c.   An exclamation point (!)

               a

---

1. Amino acids are small molecules that are the building blocks of protein

    a.   A period (.)
    b.   A question mark (?)
    c.   An exclamation point (!)

               _____

2. Are sharks mammals

    a.   A period (.)
    b.   A question mark (?)
    c.   An exclamation point (!)

               _____

3. Turn the radio down

    a.   A period (.)
    b.   A question mark (?)
    c.   An exclamation point (!)

               _____

4. Why do leaves change color in the fall

   a. A period (.)
   b. A question mark (?)
   c. An exclamation point (!)

   _____

5. I hope this bus stops at Delancy

   a. A period (.)
   b. A question mark (?)
   c. An exclamation point (!)

   _____

6. If confronted by humans, some female elephants will charge, but males often simply walk away

   a. A period (.)
   b. A question mark (?)
   c. An exclamation point (!)

   _____

7. Is Banff National Park in the Canadian Rockies

   a. A period (.)
   b. A question mark (?)
   c. An exclamation point (!)

   _____

8. At the Elephant Hills Hotel in Victoria Falls, Zimbabwe, golfers often have to share the course with baboons and impala

   a. A period (.)
   b. A question mark (?)
   c. An exclamation point (!)

   _____

9. He asked me if I had ever been to Burma

   a. A period (.)
   b. A question mark (?)
   c. An exclamation point (!)

   _____

10. One of the questions on our religion exam had to do with the tenets of Buddhism

     a.   A period (.)
     b.   A question mark (?)
     c.   An exclamation point (!)

_____

EXERCISE 64: EDITING FOR CORRECTNESS – DASHES AND PARENTHESES

CORRESPONDS TO SECTION 55 IN *THE NEW MCGRAW-HILL HANDBOOK* AND SECTIONS 62D AND 62E IN *A WRITER'S RESOURCE*

USING CATALYST	www.mhhe.com/nmhh www.mhhe.com/awr
For information and exercises on dashes, go to **Editing > Dashes** For information and exercises on parentheses, go to **Editing > Parentheses**	

Instructions: Some of the sentences below need a dash (two hyphens), and others need parentheses. Write in either the dashes or the parentheses where they are needed.

EXAMPLE

John Wayne's final film *The Shootist* deals with an aging gunman dying of cancer.

John Wayne's final <u>film--*The Shootist*--deals</u> with an aging gunman dying of cancer.

---

1. There are four steps in the writing process gathering information, drafting, revising, and editing.

2. There's only one sport I bet on professional wrestling.

3. Walt Whitman he once worked for the *Brooklyn Eagle* was honored at the Journalism Hall of Fame.

4. Philadelphia the word is Greek for "brotherly love" was first settled by the Quakers.

5. Three languages German, Italian, and French are spoken in Switzerland.

6. New York the city was once called New Amsterdam was originally a Dutch colony.

7. We need to buy quite a few things for our trip film, suntan lotion, dark glasses, and junk food.

8. The coach told the team they had only one goal "Win!"

9. Because of our gossipy neighbors, our phone it was on a party line was always busy.

10. During the Spanish Civil War a prelude to World War II, as some historians note both Germany and Italy supported the cause of General Francisco Franco.

EXERCISE 65: EDITING FOR CORRECTNESS – CAPITALIZATION

CORRESPONDS TO SECTION 57 IN *THE NEW MCGRAW-HILL HANDBOOK* AND SECTION 63 IN *A WRITER'S RESOURCE*

Using Catalyst	www.mhhe.com/nmhh www.mhhe.com/awr
For information and exercises on capitalization, go to Editing > Capitalization	

Instructions: Capitalize words as appropriate in the sentences below. Write over the letters that need capitalization.

EXAMPLE

the movie on television was boring, but I watched it anyway.

<u>The</u> movie on television was boring, but I watched it anyway.

---

1. The alexander library was just remodeled.

2. many of the trees along this street are elms.

3. We usually hold our family reunion on memorial day.

4. You can find italian wines in every price range.

5. the two doctors discussed the problem for several hours.

6. Grace was very upset about receiving a C in math 235.

7. Every summer my parents go camping in the smoky mountains.

8. Liberty park is overpopulated with canada geese.

9. Wilson comes from the south, but he grew up in the west.

10. There are many civil war battlefields in Virginia.

EXERCISE 66: EDITING FOR CORRECTNESS – CAPITALIZATION

CORRESPONDS TO SECTION 57 IN *THE NEW MCGRAW-HILL HANDBOOK* AND SECTION 63 IN *A WRITER'S RESOURCE*

USING CATALYST	www.mhhe.com/nmhh www.mhhe.com/awr
For information and exercises on capitalization, go to Editing > Capitalization	

Instructions: Capitalize words as appropriate in the sentences below. Write over the letters that need capitalization.

EXAMPLE

Some holidays fall on different days each year, but christmas is always december 25.

Some holidays fall on different days each year, but <u>Christmas</u> is always <u>December</u> 25.

---

1. My best friend's father works on rocket ships for nasa.

2. I usually do my laundry on friday.

3. The professor teaching american literature II this semester always assigns *For whom the bell tolls.*

4. Next summer I hope to visit my family in the east.

5. Colleen went to bowling green in Ohio for her undergraduate work.

6. In the early days of the nfl there weren't as many teams as there are today.

7. This year independence day falls on a saturday.

8. When I was young, my favorite movie was *The red balloon.*

9. Mary grew tired of the new england winters and moved to florida.

10. West point is located on the banks of the Hudson river.

EXERCISE 67: EDITING FOR CORRECTNESS – CAPITALIZATION

CORRESPONDS TO SECTION 57 IN *THE NEW MCGRAW-HILL HANDBOOK* AND SECTION 63 IN *A WRITER'S RESOURCE*

USING CATALYST	www.mhhe.com/nmhh www.mhhe.com/awr
For information and exercises on capitalization, go to Editing > Capitalization	

Instructions: Capitalize words as appropriate in the sentences below. Write over the letters that need capitalization.

EXAMPLE

The bagel store on Maple Street has a larger variety than Barry's bagels on Main Street.

The bagel store on Maple Street has a larger variety than Barry's <u>Bagels</u> on Main Street.

---

1. When grandmother is home, we always eat large meals.

2. The bible and the koran are often discussed in a literary context, but both books are collections of sacred writings dealing with god.

3. After a great deal of thought, Sam registered for advanced biology II for the fall semester.

4. The republican party obviously takes its name from its belief in a republican form of government.

5. Bob Hope worked for the National broadcasting company for more than six decades.

6. The caricature of uncle Sam appeared sometime around the Civil War.

7. My first class was taught by professor Gardner, dean of the division of liberal arts.

8. After graduating from Central high school, Doris attended a technical school.

9. Most of my classes meet in Miller hall.

10. The Edison phonograph company was the first to make records.

EXERCISE 68: EDITING FOR CORRECTNESS – NUMBERS AND ITALICS

CORRESPONDS TO SECTION 60 IN *THE NEW MCGRAW-HILL HANDBOOK* AND SECTION 66 IN *A WRITER'S RESOURCE*

USING CATALYST	www.mhhe.com/nmhh www.mhhe.com/awr
For information and exercises on italics, go to Editing > Italics	

Instructions: Do the sentences below use numbers and italics correctly? If not, rewrite the incorrect numbers; underline the words that should be italicized.

EXAMPLE
I usually get up at five-thirty every morning. I usually get up at <u>5:30</u> every morning.

1. There were 9 large theaters in this town in the 1950s.

2. 112 of the city's restaurants have been cited for health violations.

3. Manhattan was supposedly purchased from the Lenape Indians for twenty-four dollars in beads.

4. Richard Wright's novel, Native Son, was both critically and commercially successful.

5. The word salary originally meant salt.

6. After the flood subsided, the house was filled with fourteen feet of mud.

7. Harvey was one of the films in which Jimmy Stewart established his reputation as a brilliant actor.

8. Over the years Life magazine has captured many important people and exciting events on film.

9. Rick once had six hundred and fifty-five records.

10. My dentist bill was two thousand five hundred and sixty-three dollars--ouch!

EXERCISE 69: EDITING FOR CORRECTNESS – HYPHENS

CORRESPONDS TO SECTION 62 IN *THE NEW MCGRAW-HILL HANDBOOK* AND SECTION 67 IN *A WRITER'S RESOURCE*

USING CATALYST	www.mhhe.com/nmhh www.mhhe.com/awr
For information and exercises on hyphens, go to Editing > Hyphens	

Instructions: Which one of the sentences in each set is correct? Write the letter of the correct sentence in the space to the right.

EXAMPLE

a. A well kept garden is a pleasure to see.
b. A well-kept garden is a pleasure to see.
c. A well, kept garden is a pleasure to see.

b

---

1. a. Early 19th-century America gave rise to many reform-movements aimed at improving society.
   b. Early, nineteenth century America gave rise to many reform movements aimed at improving society.
   c. Early-nineteenth-century America gave rise to many reform movements aimed at improving society.

   _____

2. a. Abraham Lincoln was born in a one-room cabin in Kentucky in 1809.
   b. Abraham Lincoln was born in a one room cabin in Kentucky in 1809.
   c. Abraham Lincoln was born in a one, room cabin in Kentucky in 1809.

   _____

3. a. The Marshall Plan provided economic-aid to post World War II-Europe.
   b. The Marshall-Plan provided economic aid to post-World-War-II Europe.
   c. The Marshall Plan provided economic aid to post-World War II Europe.

   _____

4. a. As the USS Constitution sailed from its berth in Boston Harbor, a twenty-one gun salute was heard in the distance.
   b. As the USS Constitution sailed from its berth in Boston Harbor, a twenty-one-gun salute was heard in the distance.

c. As the USS Constitution sailed from its berth in Boston Harbor, a twenty one gun-salute was heard in the distance.

_____

5. a. Bob Hope once played Jimmy Walker, the ex-mayor of New York, in a movie.
   b. Bob Hope once played Jimmy Walker, the exmayor of New York, in a movie.
   c. Bob Hope once played Jimmy Walker, the ex mayor of New York, in a movie.

_____

6. a. Mark Twain once served as the editor in chief of a small newspaper in Virginia City, Nevada.
   b. Mark Twain once served as the editor-in-chief of a small newspaper in Virginia City, Nevada.
   c. Mark Twain once served as the editor in chief of a small-newspaper in Virginia City, Nevada.

_____

7. a. Albert is an expert on preCivil War photography.
   b. Albert is an expert on pre Civil War photography.
   c. Albert is an expert on pre-Civil War photography.

_____

8. a. Fifty-seven types of birds have been spotted in this park.
   b. Fifty seven types of birds have been spotted in this park.
   c. Fiftyseven types of birds have been spotted in this park.

_____

9. a. Air fares to Europe can be very inexpensive in the off season.
   b. Air fares to Europe can be very inexpensive in the off-season.
   c. Air fares to Europe can be very inexpensive in the offseason.

_____

10. a. Robert Redford got his start in acting doing off-Broadway plays and bit parts in television dramas.
    b. Robert Redford got his start in acting doing off Broadway plays and bit parts in television dramas.
    c. Robert Redford got his start in acting doing off-Broadway-plays and bit parts in television dramas.

_____

EXERCISE 70: EDITING FOR CORRECTNESS – SPELLING

CORRESPONDS TO SECTION 63 IN *THE NEW MCGRAW-HILL HANDBOOK* AND SECTION 68 IN *A WRITER'S RESOURCE*

USING CATALYST	www.mhhe.com/nmhh www.mhhe.com/awr
For information and exercises on spelling, go to Editing > Spelling	

Instructions: Check the sentences below for spelling. If all the words are spelled correctly, write *C* in the space to the right. If any words are spelled incorrectly, write the correct spelling in the space.

EXAMPLE

When Mary Beth marrys Bryan, it will be a day to celebrate.   *marries*

---

1. Michelangelo's most beautiful work has to be the cieling of the Sistine Chapel.

    _____

2. We mailed them a card, but they never recieved it.

    _____

3. Many immigrants came to America hopping for a better life than the one they had left behind.

    _____

4. Rudyard Kipling was the most fameous writer of his era.

    _____

5. Before the summer began, workers painted all the bench's in the park green.

    _____

6. The entire party dinned at Palumbo's in Philadelphia.

    _____

7. The nation of Germany was once a large collection of seperate countries.

    _____

8. There was an entire wall of shelfs behind my desk.

    _____

9. My parents always payed for everything with cash.

_____

10. Ian Fleming created James Bond, the suave British secret agent with a "lisense to kill."

_____

EDITING EXERCISE 12: EDITING FOR CORRECTNESS – PROBLEMS WITH PUNCTUATION

CORRESPONDS TO SECTIONS 51–56 IN *THE NEW MCGRAW-HILL HANDBOOK* AND SECTIONS 57–62 IN *A WRITER'S RESOURCE*

Instructions: Rewrite the following paragraphs in the spaces provided to eliminate problems with end punctuation, commas, semicolons, and colons.

Justinian and the Rebirth of Rome

One of the greatest Roman emperors Justinian was not born of the ruling class in fact he was the only son of a poor farmer from what is present-day Croatia Justinian rose through the ranks of the military to assume the leadership of a Roman Empire in decline and he immediately began to restore it to its former glory His army reconquered lost territories in Persia North Africa and Italy including Rome itself which had been lost to Germanic tribes in about 450 AD. Famous for orchestrating the construction of the *Hagia Sophia* in Constantinople the largest and perhaps most beautiful Christian church ever built Justinian is also remembered for producing a comprehensive codification of Roman laws the *Corpus Juris Civilis* which has proven to be influential even to this day

_____

_____

_____

_____

_____

_____

_____

_____

_____

The Age of Reform in America

Why is the early nineteenth century in the United States called the Age of Reform

This was a time when many leading American thinkers politicians and religious leaders envisioned an almost ideal society where personal morals would be improved where human misery would be alleviated and where social inequality would be eliminated Actually there were several reform movements during this period but they all shared a belief in the perfectibility of society. Spurred by the need to maintain stability and moral order in a free society the reformers sought to prohibit alcohol and gambling two vices which they believed caused great suffering and threatened the stability of the American family to provide for public education the source they believed of a truly enlightened nation and to rehabilitate criminals through prison reform. Some reformers organized to address problems of people suffering from disease disability or poverty through the establishment of better facilities and procedures for handling the sick or mentally ill Radical reformers argued for the abolishment of slavery and the equality of the sexes. Although the reform movement failed to achieve a perfect human society it did leave a lasting impact on the nation.

_____

_____

_____

_____

_____

_____

_____

_____

Copernicus's Center of the Universe

Copernicus the sixteenth-century astronomer and mathematician who studied and lectured at the Jagellonian University in Krakow Poland is famous for his heliocentric theory which places the sun at the center of the universe. In opposition to the theory promulgated by the Greek Ptolemy and his followers Copernicus theorized that all the planets including the Earth, revolve around the sun. However the real theme of the life of Copernicus is the struggle against prevailing wisdom and against that which seemed to be perfectly obvious the Sun the planets and all the other heavenly bodies revolved around the Earth. In fact this "heliocentric" theory was first proposed in the third-century BC by the Greek astronomer Aristarchus of Samos. Nicolaus Koppernigk who was born in 1473 and who Latinized his name to Copernicus revived Aristarchus' theory in a book that was quickly suppressed by the Church as "false and altogether opposed to Holy Scripture." Despite the resistance to

Copernicus's work the heliocentric theory did prevail in the end The first printed copy of
Copernicus' book reached him on his deathbed in 1543.

_____

_____

_____

_____

_____

_____

_____

_____

CORRESPONDS TO SECTIONS 54, 55, AND 61 IN *THE NEW MCGRAW-HILL HANDBOOK* AND SECTIONS 60, 61, AND 62 IN *A WRITER'S RESOURCE*

Instructions: Rewrite the following paragraphs in the spaces provided by inserting quotation marks, parentheses, dashes, and apostrophes as needed.

Americas Sweetheart: Mary Pickford

By the time Mary Pickford signed her first motion picture contract she had begun her stage career at age six! she already had ten years of acting experience. Her new boss, D. W. Griffith, agreed to pay her an unheard of salary of ten dollars a day. Several years later, at the height of her career, she commanded million-dollar contracts. Pickfords husband, Douglas Fairbanks, her good friend Charlie Chaplin, and her old boss Griffith eventually teamed up to start their own studio they gave it a very apt name: United Artists. In a twenty-three year career, Pickford made close to two-hundred films and, in 1929, won the first Oscar ever presented to an actress. Known as Americas Sweetheart, she would become one of the most famous women of her time, as well as one of the wealthiest.

_____

_____

_____

_____

_____

_____

_____

_____

_____

The Gutenberg Bible

Problems with tracing the history of Johann Gutenberg 1397-1468 arise partly because the printers name appears on none of his works. Much of what we know of Gutenbergs life comes down to us through official documents concerning lawsuits. The man credited with the invention of the printing press it is believed by many to be the first to use movable type was on several occasions the subject of lawsuits. To some degree, however, these suits helped to establish the details concerning Gutenbergs first press. He was first sued in 1438 by his late partners family, who introduced into evidence facts about the development of a new and secret process by which to print. In 1449, Gutenberg found a new partner he had won the lawsuit brought by his first partners family who backed the publication of a bible This Gutenberg Bible is considered the first substantial printed matter to come from the new press. However, his new partner, an attorney, brought and won another lawsuit against Gutenberg, and he became the printing companys sole owner in 1455. Thus, although the Gutenberg Bible was a critical success, it was a business failure.

_____

_____

_____

_____

_____

_____

_____

_____

_____

Joseph Conrad

One of the most celebrated writers in the English language, Joseph Conrad was born in Poland in 1857. At age sixteen, he began his career as a merchant seaman the sea plays an important role in many of his novels apprenticing in the French merchant marine in Marseille. Eventually he moved to England, where after more than two decades at sea he rose to the rank of ships master in the British merchant service. In 1886, he became a British subject changing his name from Jozef Teodor Konrad Nalecz Koreniowski to Joseph Conrad. With the publication of his third novel in 1897, Conrads skill as a writer was clear and he left the sailors life for good. Although critical acclaim came early, popular acclaim for Conrads novels came only a short time before his death in 1924 the same is true of his financial success. Four of his most important novels are *Lord Jim*, *Nostromo*, *The Heart* of *Darkness*, and *Victory*. Of this Polish-born virtuoso in English, one critic has said: A master at creating character and atmosphere, [he] acutely portrayed individuals suffering from isolation and moral disintegration, and the clash between...cultures.

EDITING EXERCISE 14: EDITING FOR CORRECTNESS – PROBLEMS WITH MECHANICS

CORRESPONDS TO SECTIONS 57, 59, 60, 62, AND 63 IN *THE NEW MCGRAW-HILL HANDBOOK* AND SECTIONS 63 AND 65–68 IN *A WRITER'S RESOURCE*

Instructions: Rewrite the following paragraphs in the spaces provided to correct problems with capitalization, spelling, hyphenation, numbers, and italics.

Picasso: Learning to Paint like a Child

Pablo Picasso once said that when he was four years old he could paint as well as any of the great french masters, but it took him a lifetime to learn "to paint like a child." The process of learning to paint like a child was a life long endevor. Picasso, whose Father was a drawing instructor, was born in spain in eighteen eighty one seemingly with a pencil and paintbrush in his hand. At the age of nineteen, he moved to Paris where he joined other poverty striken painters who were trying to establish themselves as world famous artists. While best remembered as an inventor of cubism, initially Picasso built his fame on his Blue Period paintings, works completed between 1901 and 1904, in which the themes of sickness, hunger, and solatude have a profound presence. The Paintings of this time are almost monocrome in thier use of blue paint, which has been attributed both to the poverty and sorrow visible in his specter like figures and to the poverty of the artist, who could afford only laundry blueing as a pigment to his otherwise inexpensive white paint.

_____

_____

_____

_____

_____

_____

_____

_____

Aesop's Fables

Teaching clear and specific lessons, Aesops fables are short tales in which the characters are animals. According to legend, Aesop was for many years a slave on the greek island of samos. He was eventually freed and spent the rest of his life travelling before his execution in the city of delphi for insulting the oracle. However, since the renaissance, scholars have doubted the actual existance of Aesop, for it seems that what is accepted as his biography has more in common with characters from greek tradgedy than with any historical person. In short, the name *aesop* was a convenent way to acount for the authorship of many traditional stories and peices of folk wisdom, many of which were probably passed down in oral form many centurys before Aesop's time. A book entitled Aesop's Fables was first collected in the 2nd or 3rd century AD, and since that time these often told stories have remained classic works of litrature.

_____

_____

_____

_____

_____

_____

_____

_____

_____

Watches

One of the most common, and certainly one of the most practical pieces of jewerly, the wristwatch appeared in the early part of the twentieth-century. Watches themselves date all the way back to fiftenth century europe; a spring mechanism was first used as a source of power. Prior to that time, clocks depended upon complicated systems of wieghts to measure time. The main-spring allowed clockmakers to produce portable clocks, and eventually, as technology advanced, small watches that could be worn as articles of jewlry. The first watches, six inch high contraptions, were made of iron and were worn around the neck or waiste. Unlike contemporary versions, they had one handed faces, so they were inaccurate. In the 1600s, pocket watches first appeared. They would serve as the primary method of telling time for the next two centuries, and only by the start of the twentieth-century would wristwatches begin to replace the classic pocket watch as the standard of time.

_____

_____

_____

_____

_____

_____

_____

_____

The Potato Blight

Brought to europe from the new world, potatos seemed like the ideal crop. They were easy to grow and could be stored for long periods without spoiling. Enough potatos could be produced on a small peice of land to feed a family, and the potato was rich in nutreints and protien. By the mid nineteenth-century most of the people in Ireland would depend on the potato crop for thier livelihoods and thier lives. Ireland had become a one crop nation, and the qualities of potatos had forced a concentration on this crop over all others. The average male ate 2 to 4 pounds of potatos every day. In eighteen fourty five, tradgedy struck. In that year a fungus, accidentally transported from america, wipped out the potato crop. For the next five years, the fungus ravaged the potato crop, and over 1,000,000 people died of starvation and its accompanying diseases. Another 1,000,000 people were forced to flee Ireland to escape what became known as "the great hunger." By the time the potato blight had run its coarse, the population of Ireland had declined twenty five percent.

_____

_____

_____

_____

_____

_____

Our Best Friends

Dogs have served as loyal helpers and friendly companions to Human Beings for almost fourteen thousand years now. In fact, dogs are one of the first animals to be domesticated. In comparison, goats, horses, cattle, chickens, and other livstock were domesticated only about seven thousand years ago. Scientists have traced the earliest dogs back to a small, weesel like mammal that roamed the plains of asia more than sixty million years ago. Today there are more than four hundred breeds of dogs, all the products of ages of genetic engineering. Since the first dogs were taken in by people, they have served as hunters, protectors, herders, beasts of burden, and most importantly, as companions. Modern society has often deemed the dog as an equal, a loyal and trusted friend. In anceint egypt, however, the dog enjoyed devine status; it was considered sacred. Most recently dogs have come to play invaluble roles as guides to the blind, agents of the law and even therapists in some situations.

_____

_____

_____

_____

_____

_____

_____

_____

_____

Galileo

An italian physicist and astronomer, Galileo Galilei was born in pisa, italy in 1564. Galileo began his studies in Medicine, but soon abandoned them in favor of Math. At 25, Galileo became a professor of mathematics at the university of pisa. There he worked on the formulation of the laws of motion. Some of his free fall experiments involved drooping various objects from the tower of pisa. He is supposed to have drooped a canonball and a small bullet at the same time to demonstrate that objects of different wieghts would acheive the same aceleration while faling. Galileo also developed the thermameter. Often credited with invention of the telescope, Galileo actually built his own telescope after hearing of the invention of a very rudimentary-telescope in Holland. With his telescope, galileo discovered 4 of jupiter's moons, proved the existence of sunspots, explored the surface of the moon, described the phases of venus, and mapped the milky way. Near the end of his life galileo angered the roman catholic hierarchy because of his defence of Copernicus' heliocentric theory, which placed the sun in the centre of the universe. In 1633, he was sentenced to life imprisonment for his beliefs, but that sentence was quickly commuted to house arrest. His final works were smugled to holland for publication. While still under arrest, he died in 1642.

_____

_____

_____

_____

_____

_____

_____

_____

Name_____

Date_____

Course_____

POSTTEST

Items 1–5: Sentence Parts

Instructions: The following items ask you to identify various parts of a sentence. Write your answers in the spaces provided.

EXAMPLE

Find a conjunction:

The soldiers had marched all night, and they were tired.   _____*and*

---

1. **Find the sentence's subject and verb:**

   During her childhood, Anna studied the piano.   _____   _____
                                                         subj   verb

2. **Find a pronoun and an adverb:**

   The man, whom the police recently arrested,
   does not have a criminal record.   _____   _____
                                            pron   adv

3. **Find an adjective and a preposition:**

   He left the windows open in subzero weather.   _____   _____
                                                        adj   pron

4. **Find a subordinate clause:**

   In World War I, Austria-Hungary fought on the side of Germany, which was at war with the Allies.

   _____

5. **Find a main clause:**

   Charles, who never tires of praising himself, has a fantastic imagination.

   _____

Items 6–20: Sentence Structure and Logic

Instructions: The following items contain three versions of the same sentence or sentences. Write the letter of the best version on the line to the right.

EXAMPLE

a. A bear ate our food while we camped in the woods.
b. While camping in the woods, our food was eaten by a bear.
c. Our food was eaten by a bear while camping in the woods.

_____ *a*

---

6.   a. Pete wore a hat on his head with suntan lotion.
        b. Pete wore suntan lotion and a hat on his head.
        c. On his head, Pete wore a hat with suntan lotion.

_____

7.   a. The patient paced up and down the hall waiting for the results of his x-ray.
        b. The patient, waiting for the results of his x-ray, paced up and down the hall.
        c. Up and down the hall waiting for the results of his x- ray the patient paced.

_____

8.   a. Computers have always fascinated her, someday she hopes to be an engineer.
        b. Computers have always fascinated her. Someday she hopes to be an engineer.
        c. Computers have always fascinated her someday she hopes to be an engineer.

_____

9.   a. The results of the experiment were confusing, for they could be interpreted in several ways.
        b. The results of the experiment were confusing, they could be interpreted in several ways.
        c. The results of the experiment were confusing they could be interpreted in several ways.

_____

10.   a. Anetta loves living in Chicago nonetheless, she misses her family desperately.
        b. Anetta loves living in Chicago, nonetheless, she misses her family desperately.
        c. Anetta loves living in Chicago; nonetheless, she misses her family desperately.

_____

11.   a. Follow recipes if you want to bake delicious desserts.
        b. Recipes should be followed to bake delicious desserts.
        c. To bake delicious desserts, recipes should be followed.

_____

12.   a. Angola is a small country in Africa, which is a large continent.
        b. Angola is a small country in Africa; which is a large continent.
        c. Angola is a small country in Africa. Which is a large continent.

_____

13.   a. Hindi is spoken in India, it is not the only language of that country.
            b. Hindi is spoken in India it is not the only language of that country.
            c. Although Hindi is spoken in India, it is not the only language of that country.

                                                        _____

14.   a. A large snake bit the child as he returned to camp.
            b. A large snake bit the child. As he returned to camp.
            c. A large snake bit the child, he was returning to camp.

                                                        _____

15.   a. Over the foggy plains ran the buffaloes in the mist a lone hunter waited.
            b. Over the foggy plains ran the buffaloes in the mist, a lone hunter waited.
            c. Over the foggy plains ran the buffaloes; in the mist, a lone hunter waited.

                                                        _____

16.   a. The airliner skidded off the runway, more than a hundred passengers were injured.
            b. The airliner skidded off the runway. More than a hundred passengers were injured.
            c. The airliner skidded off the runway more than a hundred passengers were injured.

                                                        _____

17.   a. The ski detached from Joanne's boot while skiing down the long slope.
            b. Joanne's ski detached from her boot while skiing down the long slope.
            c. While she skied down the long slope, Joanne's ski detached from her boot.

                                                        _____

18.   a. I have seen three frightening forest fires, two horrifying tornadoes, and one terrifying blizzard.
            b. I have seen three forest fires that were frightening, two horrifying tornadoes, and one terrifying blizzard.
            c. I have seen three forest fires that were frightening, two horrifying tornadoes, and one blizzard that was terrifying.

                                                        _____

19.   a. Celery is low in calories, high in fiber, and it is not hard to digest.
            b. Celery is low in calories, high in fiber, and easy to digest.
            c. Celery is low in calories, high in fiber, and digesting it is easy.

                                                        _____

20.   a. Your journal, your in-class writing, homework, and participation are important in this course.
            b. Your journal, in-class writing, your homework, and participation are important in this course.
            c. Your journal, in-class writing, homework, and participation are important in this course.

                                                        _____

Items 21–35: Correct Usage

Correct any problems you find in the following sentences by rewriting the part of the sentence that is incorrect. Place your corrections in the spaces to the right. If the sentence is correct, write *C* in the space. <u>Note:</u> You may have to change or add words.

EXAMPLE

Save the planet: our children's future depend on it.

depends

---

21. Bill and Angela is expecting to leave soon. _____

22. The entire team are on the field. _____

23. Ari's friend and confidant is Melissa. _____

24. The water samples contains heavy metal and chlorine. _____

25. The Society of Mechanical Engineers recommend this process. _____

26. Everyone have been asked to contribute. _____

27. Either Jason or his family have been named in the lawsuit. _____

28. Each of the students own a computer. _____

29. Neither Arlene nor Fanny know how to speak Arabic. _____

30. People who eat as little as she does risks damaging their health. _____

31. By the time Anton returned to Warsaw, the street on which he once lived was renamed. _____

32. After she had lived in Paris, she moves to Hong Kong. _____

33. Them playing the radio loudly is getting on my nerves. _____

34. Eileen and him have gotten engaged. _____

35. Whose that young boy who resembles you? _____

Items 36–45: Punctuation, Spelling, and Mechanics

Instructions: Correct the following sentences by adding or removing punctuation, correcting spelling, or making other changes. Rewrite each sentence correctly on the lines that follow it.

EXAMPLE

Mythology is one way a culture explanes its values.

Mythology is one way a culture explains its values.

---

36. Be quiet, or the guards will throw us out.

_____

37. The child asked, Will it ever stop raining

_____

38. He suffers from arthritis so he can't climb stairs.

_____

39. Paraguay is not in europe; it is in south america.

_____

40. The hotel's in Hawaii are quite beautiful.

_____

41. If it is convient, please call before six o'clock.

_____

42. The copyeditor looked at her ink stained fingers as she put down the manuscript for
    Heartburn Hotel, a new novel.

_____

_____

43. He spent two months pay on that ring!

_____

44. There were only 2 students still writing, when I left the examination room.

_____

45. He had but one true love himself.

_____

Items 46–47: Writing Essays

Instructions: Read each item carefully. Then choose the best response, and write its letter in
the space to the right.

46. Which of the following would make the best thesis statement for an essay of between
    500 and 750 words?

203

a. Learning math can be difficult, but it is important.

b. Strong math skills are imperative for people majoring in engineering, computer science, and economics.

c. Strong math skills are important whatever the student's academic major.

_____

47. Which sentence does not belong in the paragraph? Write its letter in the space provided.

(a) Technology has invaded the contemporary American home. (b) The typical kitchen boasts a self-cleaning oven, a microwave, and a dishwasher. (c) Some even come equipped with ice-making, water-dispensing refrigerators. (d) The television has evolved into the "entertainment center," complete with a CD player, a VCR, and, of course, a large-screen, remotely controlled color boob-tube. (e) Hand-operated mixers and washboards are, of course, still sold in hardware stores, and some people refuse to give up their dial telephones. (f) Many people would be lost without their computers, fax machines, electronic treadmills, and high-tech telephones.

_____

Items 48–50: Writing Research Papers

Read the following entry from *Wilson Humanities Abstracts,* and answer the questions that follow. Write the correct answers in the spaces provided

AUTHOR: Stocks, Denys A.
  TITLE: Making stone vessels in ancient Mesopotamia and Egypt
  SOURCE: Antiquity (ISSN:0003-598X) v 67 p 596-603 September '93
CONTAINS: bibliography; illustration(s)
 	
SUBJECTS COVERED:
Drilling and boring
Experimental archaeology
Mesopotamia/Antiquities

48. In what periodical was the article listed in this entry published?   _____

49. In what year was this article published?   _____

50. In the spaces below, write an entry for this article as it would appear in a references page, which uses the American Psychological Association (APA) format.

_____

_____

End of Posttest

Answer Key to Exercises 1–70

(Possible answers to the Editing Exercises and answers to the pretest and posttest are available on the instructor's site of www.mhhe.com/nmhh or www.mhhe.com/awr.)

Exercise 1
1. c   2. c   3. b   4. a   5. a   6. b   7. b   8. a   9. b   10. b

Exercise 2
Answers will vary.

Exercise 3
1. 4   2. 5   3. 4   4. 1   5. 4   6. 6   7. 1   8. 3   9. 4   10. 3
11. 5/7   12. 3   13. 3   14. 5/8   15. 7

Exercise 4
1. 2/6/7/9   2. 2/5/6/8   3. 3/7   4. even   5. 2/3/5/6/9   6. 4/6/7
7. 3/4/6/7   8. 2/4/5/7/8   9. that   10. 5/6/8

Exercise 5
1. c   2. a   3. c   4. a   5. c   6. b   7. c   8. b   9. d   10. b
11. c   12. a   13. b   14. b   15. b   16. d   17. b   18. c   19. b   20. a

Exercise 6
1. a   2. c   3. a   4. a   5. b

Exercise 7
1. f   2. c   3. a   4. a

Exercise 8
1. c   2. a   3. a   4. b   5. c   6. a   7. a   8. c   9. c   10. b
11. a   12. b   13. b   14. c   15. b

Exercise 9
1. a   2. c   3. b   4. a   5. c

Exercise 10
1. c   2. b   3. b   4. c   5. c

Exercise 11
1. rain   2. jealousy/emotion   3. mountains/Tennessee   4. he *or* it   5. His   6. they/we
7. whom/I   8. southern   9. favorite   10. jade/tiny   11. extremely   12. very
13. terribly/suddenly   14. long/very   15. emerged   16. won   17. heard/ignored
18. opposed/established   19. and   20. Because   21. but   22. in   23. to   24. around
25. in   26. the   27. an   28. the   29. Religion   30. Isaac Newton

Exercise 12
1. was   2. will   3. will   4. is   5. were   6. will   7. is/has been   8. are   9. will   10. will

Exercise 13
1. personal   2. indefinite   3. demonstrative   4. relative   5. reflexive
6. relative   7. personal   8. relative   9. indefinite   10. personal

Exercise 14
1. tank   2. most/influential   3. Greek/chief   4. Latin/diamond   5. Terrible/first
6. island/nine   7. first/Spanish/fifteen   8. Arawak   9. seventeenth/British/Spanish
10. freed/armed/new   11. Jagiellon/united   12. Old/many/serious/Babylonian
13. jumping/diverse/large   14. old-fashioned/Emerson   15. traditional/Japanese/stylized

Exercise 15
1. The earliest printing technology...used carefully carved....   2. Early printed texts....
3. Movable wooden type....   4. ...modern printing methods.   5. ....small individual pieces
of type...multiple readable impressions....Gutenberg's invention was supplanted only recently
by easier-to-use electronic technology.   6. ...an ancient Indo-Aryan language that is part of
the greater Indo-European family of languages.   7. ...in place a dominant social and cultural
system....   8. ...Sanskrit is the classical literary language of India.   9. ...it has a very
complex grammatical structure.   10. ...some original Indian literary works.

Exercise 16
1. Along the dirt road   2. to its mate   3. crying loudly for her mother   4. at Valley Forge
5. After studying Roman law   6. with several hundred elephants   7. who was born in India
8. that reflect a culture's beliefs   9. When I left home   10. after the circus leaves town   11.
Although they originated as social organizations   12. which had been in Damascus   13.
who united many small states into a nation   14. which first appeared in Europe in the twelfth
century   15. watches depended on a spring mechanism 16. Germany, Japan, and Italy were
the Axis powers   17. Margaret Atwood...has written several best sellers   18. we left early
19. Marcus Aurelius was a stoic philosopher and writer   20. he was famous in his day as an
orator and a political leader

Exercise 17
1. One of the greatest physicists and mathematicians ever. / As well as laws of motion.
2. The longest river in Italy. / A distance of 405 miles. / Depositing vast quantities of silt.
3. A primary influence on Rome. / Establishing both a strong army and a fairly large navy.
4. To demand equal rights for women. / Influential to generations of women seeking equality
with men.
5. Accidentally transported from America.
6. The smoothest and most efficient highways of the early nineteenth century. / Later, with
the invention of the steam engine.
7. Born to a family of Irish immigrants in Pennsylvania. / Robert Fulton, a friend of
Benjamin Franklin. / Was a talented painter and designer.
8. A well-ordered unit of pike-bearing infantrymen. / Stood closely and protected each other
by overlapping their shields in front of them.
9. An Italian physicist and astronomer. / Often credited with the invention of the telescope.
10. Teaching on the streets and in the open markets of Athens. / Insisting on the ignorance of
most people, including himself.

Exercise 18

1. It's impossible to find anything, the place is a real mess.   2. He wanted to summarize all knowledge, he also wanted to dispel superstition.   3. By the time he was twenty-four he was an important spokesperson for the abolition movement he published his famous biography....   4. He wanted to end capital punishment and torture, he also wanted to rehabilitate prisoners.   5. Romanticism was a nineteenth-century artistic and literary movement that valued emotion over reason intuition was more important to the Romantics....   6. The term *realism* was first used in 1850 to describe a painting by Courbet, the painting was realistic.   7. Britain developed new markets and expanded trade around the world France was isolated....   8. Weighing 30 tons and filling a 30- by 50-foot room, this computer needed 18,0000 vacuum tubes it used enough electricity to run....   9. Handheld transistor radios quickly replaced the large desktop or stand-alone models in addition, portable televisions....   10. But Serling did much more than introduce the story he was the creator of the series....

Exercise 19

1. have	2. portrays	3. C	4. contains	5. is	6. C
7. is	8. C	9. are	10. comes	11. use	12. is
13. is	14. stand	15. are	16. help	17. prevents	18. are
19. C	20. live				

Exercise 20

1. oppose	2. appear	3. close	4. is	5. lack	6. hold
7. know	8. were	9. have	10. draw	11. produces	12. has
13. C	14. attract	15. poses			

Exercise 21

1. dance	2. has	3. unite	4. are	5. connect	6. stand
7. C	8. are	9. have	10. play	11. lead	12. C
13. take	14. was	15. are			

Exercise 22

1. buys	2. imports	3. seems	4. C	5. were
6. C	7. was	8. contains	9. C	10. revolves

Exercise 23

1. C	2. has	3. was	4. contains	5. is	6. decides
7. is	8. C	9. C	10. think	11. is	12. sponsors
13. C	14. was	15. creates			

Exercise 24

1. participates	2. C	3. has	4. C	5. is	6. C
7. C	8. C	9. seems	10. has	11. was	12. listens
13. plays	14. sees	15. try			

Exercise 25

1. awakes	2. is	3. beats	4. becomes	5. begins	6. bent
7. bit	8. blew	9. broke	10. brought	11. dreamed/dreamt	
12. dealt	13. wore	14. swore	15. took		

Exercise 26
1. iced   2. used   3. bored   4. prejudiced   5. Raised
6. asked   7. used   8. used   9. confused   10. mixed

Exercise 27
1. had spoken   2. had clung   3. had caught   4. had hanged   5. C
6. has seen   7. had sewn   8. had mastered   9. C   10. had bought
11. had placed 12. has had   13. had broken 14. had been   15. will be

Exercise 28
1. get   2. were   3. avoid   4. remove   5. can
6. were   7. will   8. had been   9. had not invaded   10. had not been

Exercise 29
1. his   2. her   3. C   4. its   5. his   6. C
7. its   8. its   9. his   10. her   11. it   12. himself
13. C   14. C   15. its

Exercise 30
Possible Revisions
1. ...Jane (or Emily) told Emily (or Jane) about a strange flightless bird....   2. ...This event
led to Germany's reunification.   3. ...which ended Britain's dominion over Hong Kong.
4. The United States entered World War II when Japan attacked Pearl Harbor in 1941.
5. According to this report, inflation has not proven to be a problem lately, and the Federal
Reserve....   6. In states such as Minnesota, people are used to....   7. Korea's automobile,
appliance, and electrical equipment production signals increased industrial production.
8. Iran's carpet industry is highly profitable. Iranian carpets hold their value for generations.
9. According to the manual, users need to install an AAA battery.   10. France's grapes are
excellent, and the French export wines around the world.

Exercise 31
1. him   2. us   3. her   4. us   5. His   6. us
7. me   8. them   9. he   10. everyone's   11. its   12. Their
13. No one's   14. His   15. Everyone's

Exercise 32
1. whom   2. who   3. C   4. who   5. whom   6. C
7. whom   8. who   9. who   10. whose   11. who   12. who
13. who   14. C   15. who

Exercise 33
1. actually   2. well   3. quickly   4. fast   5. C   6. uselessly
7. confidently 8. noiselessly 9. reluctantly   10. Formerly   11. significantly   12. C
13. C   14. nearly   15. C

Exercise 34
1. good   2. well   3. bad   4. worried   5. exquisite
6. anxious   7. C   8. tired   9. angrily   10. delicious

Exercise 35
1. more colorful   2. most anxious   3. more cautious   4. more studious   5. C
6. most generous   7. most delicious   8. biggest   9. largest   10. smallest

Exercise 36
Possible Revisions
1. A famous African-American diplomat....   2. A year earlier, Bunche negotiated an agreement ending the Arab-Israeli struggle over Palestine.   3. ...and he played an important role in the San Francisco conference at which the formation of the United Nations was planned.   4. ...Bunche was asked to oversee the deployment of a United Nations peacekeeping force sent to the Suez Canal....   5. ...which was experiencing much political unrest. Four years later, Bunche used his genius to negotiate a peace between Greek and Turkish residents of Cyprus.   6. Animals have to be good at identifying their kin.   7. But in some cases they have a paradoxical need to blend in.   8. No one wants to stand out from the crowd....   9. ...they have stripes in order to confuse large predatory cats.   10. When attacked, zebras run in every direction, and the stripes make the predator feel dizzy.

Exercise 37
Possible Revisions
1. ...in July.   2. ...was a surveyor.   3. Before studying engineering, Abraham Bieden split logs and piloted rafts down the river.   4. ...believed that a railway from Cape Town to Cairo would improve transportation and commerce throughout Africa.   5. ...analyzed the mineral deposits in the soil.   6. ...tested a new anti-AIDS vaccine.   7. ...both now enjoy almost universal respect.   8. Many archeologists deny that the lost continent of Atlantis was more than a myth.   9. ...could not agree on the future of slavery or of the nation.
10. During July, the southern hemisphere is in winter.

Exercise 38
1. ...that the Etruscans....   2. ...to a Greek historian named Herodotus.   3. Herodotus believed that the Etruscans....   4. ...than that of any other people living in Italy at that time.
5. ...no other type of language we now know.   6. to the account...as intently as possible.
7. ...as one of the most devastating...in American history....   8. for a major...was as great as can be imagined.   9. ...has been and always will be...history of   10. to withstand...as horrible as the one....

Exercise 39
1. b   2. c   3. c   4. a   5. c   6. a   7. a   8. a   9. c   10. b
11. a   12. c   13. a   14. b   15. c

Exercise 40
1. became   2. responded   3. were   4. mean   5. visited   6. has shown
7. means   8. C   9. is   10. is   11. has been   12. had been
13. led   14. would have contracted   15. had been

Exercise 41
1. b   2. b   3. a   4. b   5. c   6. b   7. b   8. b   9. b   10. c

Exercise 42
1. a   2. a   3. b   4. b   5. b   6. b   7. b   8. b   9. b   10. a

Exercise 43

1. b   2. c   3. c   4. b   5. b   6. c   7. b   8. c   9. c   10. c
11. a   12. b   13. b   14. c   15. a

Exercise 44

1. c   2. c   3. b   4. c   5. b   6. b   7. a   8. c   9. a   10. a

Exercise 45

1. a   2. b   3. a   4. b   5. a   6. a   7. b   8. a   9. a   10. b

Exercise 46
Possible Revisions
1. John hit the ball.   2. Sandy hit the home run.   3. The students elected Joanne class president.   4. The quality of your essays surprised me.   5. The corporal took twenty-three enemy soldiers prisoner.   6. The animal rights activist set the laboratory rats free.   7. The parent council banned the books that students had checked out in large numbers and took them from the library shelves.   8. A master chef prepared the dinner, and a team of waiters served it.   9. Someone mistakenly filed the report under the name Harry S Truman instead of Truman, Harry.   10. Observers blamed several key executives of both Enron and Arthur Andersen for Enron's fraudulent accounting.

Exercise 47
Possible Revisions
1. Anyone who needs a loan should never borrow from my Uncle Shifty.   2. Some countries require visitors to bring a visa.   3. French chefs are famous for their culinary skills.   4. Every senator was expected to vote his or her conscience....   5. A nurse should pay attention to changes in a patient's appetite.   6. Firefighters must keep themselves in good physical condition.   7. In communist Rumania, farmers ran the risk of having their land....   8. Infantry soldiers must wear heavy packs on their backs.   9. Students enrolled in Photography I must develop their own film.   10. Anyone who has pride would never....

Exercise 48
Possible Revisions
1. When the Americans left Saigon, the North Vietnamese, against whom the US troops had fought until 1973, took control.   2. The American government knew the war in Vietnam was lost.   3. In 1954, Vietnam had been divided into the North and the South as a result of the Geneva Convention....   4. That war lasted from 1946 to 1954; the French decided they had lost too many men and too much money in the war.   5. As soon as the French left, Communist guerrillas from the North attacked the South.   6. This caused the United States to enter the war; at first it sent military advisors to support the South Vietnamese government.   7. Because the Communists were well supplied by the Russians and were better trained than the South Vietnamese soldiers, the Americans decided to send combat troops, not just advisors.   8. The Tonkin Gulf Resolution of 1964 committed even more American troops to the war, and the United States soon had enough forces in Vietnam to fight major battles. Indeed, this was a war very different from any other the United States had fought.   9. When the North launched the Tet Offensive in 1968, the Americans and the South Vietnamese suffered many casualties, and American public opinion of the war turned negative.   10. A cease-fire was signed when the two sides met in Paris in 1974; however,

the war did not come to an end until the North conquered the South, renaming Saigon, the South's former capital, Ho Chi Min City.

Exercise 49
Possible Revisions

1. lose   2. principal   3. accepted   4. stationary   5. sight/breath   6. deserts
7. You're   8. too/lightly   9. their/a lot   10. altogether/contract

Exercise 50
Possible Revisions
1. ...has always been controversial.   2. ...verbose; when speaking, he was always concise.
3. H. M. Warner was serious when....   4. ....many airlines went bankrupt in the 1980s.
5. ...knew that they had to accept the fact that their countries would be occupied by the Allies.
6. People should avoid clichés; in fact, they should always try to be original.
7. The President was asked if his wife would be involved in drafting a new budget that would force the government to decrease spending.   8. Certain government entitlement programs have strong support, but they may be eliminated by Congress.   9. The young engineer, who envied his sister's success as a stockbroker, decided to succeed by working hard.   10. Albert was absorbed as he watched a rerun of Hitchcock's film classic *Psycho* on television, but he became frightened during the famous shower scene.

Exercise 51
1. banged, the door   2. painted, her friends   3. To Helen, eating
4. As Matt cooked, Anna   5. Surprised by his wife, Roger   6. After Billy ate, the cat
7. on Monday, not Sunday   8. Winston Churchill, "the heroes fight like Greeks."
9. beach, it   10. escaped, the police

Exercise 52
1. United States, I   2. In fact, I   3. Fortunately, I   4. officer, he
5. However, it   6. China, India's   7. ago, the Himalayas   8. 1947, it
9. Pakistanis, they   10. decades, Burma

Exercise 53
1. New York, crosses...Water Gap, flows...Pennsylvania, and   2. cold, windy, and snowy
3. blood, toil, tears, and sweat,   4. Europe, Asia, and Africa.   5. writing, painting, travel, and politics.   6. China, Mongolia, and other parts of Asia.   7. North Africa, to Southern Italy, and eventually to all other parts of Europe.   8. 1361-63, 1369-71, 1374-75, 1390, and 1400.   9. Queen Eleanor of Aragon, King Alfonso XI of Castile, the daughter of King Edward III of England, and two Canterbury archbishops.   10. a shortage of skilled and peasant labor, a reduction in the amount of land that could be cultivated, and an increase in wages for artisans and peasants alike.

Exercise 54
1. parties, but   2. Poland, and   3. 1729, yet   4. horse, and   5. hot, for
6. loudly, yet   7. beings, for   8. spiders, but   9. them, so   10. prepared, or

Exercise 55
1. poisonous, yellowish-brown   2. clear, loud   3. long, heavy   4. dry, mountainous

5. old, gnarled   6. beautiful, rhythmic   7. C   8. C   9. C   10. dramatic, ice-capped

Exercise 56
1. C   2. New York City, which was originally called New Amsterdam, was....   3. The Taj Mahal, which is in India, was....   4. C   5. Babe Ruth, the famous Yankee baseball player, began....   6. C   7. C   8. The passenger pigeon, which was once very common, has....
9. C   10. Rhodes, a beautiful Greek island, was....

Exercise 57
1. Denver, Colorado   2. July 27, 1996   3. 300,000 miles/90,000   4. 1,000,000 dollars (*or* $1 million)   5. Gettysburg, Pennsylvania   6. Manitoba, Canada   7. Phil Osophie, MA and Rosetta Stone, PhD   8. Dr. Martin Luther King, Jr.   9. Laura Litigious, Esq and Daryl Dentum, DDS/November 15, 1997.   10. 5,000/Fr. Joseph Andreas, SJ/Monterey, Mexico.

Exercise 58
1. Monrovia is....   2. The Oder River flows....   3. ...a farmer and an architect.   4. Thomas Jefferson was also....   5. ...was surrounded by fields...   6. The deep, blue water....   7. ...Southwest because of the hot, dry climate there.   8. President Roosevelt looked thin and tired....   9. I enjoy reading Edgar Allan Poe....   10. Alex often visits....

Exercise 59
1. John Burroughs, the naturalist; Henry Ford, the automobile manufacturer; and Harvey Firestone, the rubber manufacturer   2. unsinkable; nevertheless   3. adventure; later
4. kings; they were   5. Europe; as a matter   6. morning; the bridge   7. poetry; he also translated   8. colony; in 1997   9. 1912; however   10. 1929; as a result

Exercise 60
1. ...dessert: apple pie.   2. ...sights: the Statue of Liberty....   3. 3:00 p.m.   4. ...trust: she was their savior.   5. ....bluntly: "I can't fix this car."   6. ...Turkey: the Euphrates....
7. ...to succeed: energy, courage, and perseverance.   8. ...passions: family, work, and opera.
9. ...room: "You all had ample opportunity to murder Sir Charles."   10. C

Exercise 61
1. *Day's*   2. highway's   3. Nadeem's   4. it's   5. its
6. A's/B's   7. FBI's   8.UCLA's   9. nations   10. its

Exercise 62
1. "Be careful about reading health books," said Mark Twain. "You may die of a misprint."
2. ..."License to Steal."   3. "Show me a hero," said F. Scott Fitzgerald, "and I'll write you a tragedy."   4. "Every being," noted Simone Weil, "cries out silently to be read differently."
5. "Mack the Knife" was recorded....   6. According to my professor, "Bartleby the Scrivener" by Herman Melville....   7. "Headless Body Found in Topless Bar" has to be....
8. Bill said, "I was surprised to hear Mary shout 'Fire!'"   9. "Please all, and you will please none," said Aesop.   10. Edgar Allan Poe sold his poem "The Raven" for about ten dollars.

Exercise 63
1. a   2. b   3. c   4. b   5. a   6. a   7. b   8. c   9. a   10. a

Exercise 64

1. process--gathering   2. on--professional wrestling   3. Walt Whitman (he once worked for the *Brooklyn Eagle*) was honored....   4. Philadelphia (the word is Greek for "brotherly love") was first settled....   5. Three languages--German, Italian, and French--are....
6. New York (the city was once called New Amsterdam) was....   7. ...for our trip--film, suntan lotion....   8. one goal--"Win!"   9. ...our phone (it was on a party line) was always busy.   10. During the Spanish Civil War--a prelude to World War II, as some historians note--both Germany....

Exercise 65

1. Alexander Library   2. Many   3. Memorial Day   4. Italian
5. The two doctors   6. Math 235   7. Smoky Mountains   8. Liberty Park/Canada
9. South/West   10. Civil War

Exercise 66

1. NASA   2. Friday   3. American Literature II/*For Whom the Bell Tolls*
4. East   5. Bowling Green   6. NFL   7. Independence Day/Saturday
8. *The Red Balloon*   9. New England/Florida   10. West Point/Hudson River

Exercise 67

1. Grandmother   2. Bible/Koran/God   3. Biology II   4. Republican Party   5. National Broadcasting Company   6. Uncle Sam   7. Professor Gardner/dean of the Division of Liberal Arts   8. Central High School   9. Miller Hall   10. Edison Phonograph Company

Exercise 68

1. nine   2. One hundred twelve   3. correct   4. Native Son   5. salary
6. correct   7. Harvey   8. Life   9. 655   10. $2,563

Exercise 69

1. c   2. a   3. c   4. b   5. a   6. b   7. c   8. a   9. b   10. a

Exercise 70

1. ceiling   2. received   3. hoping   4. famous   5. benches
6. dined   7. separate   8. shelves   9. paid   10. license